SPELLING 4

FOR YOUNG CATHOLICS

WRITTEN BY
SETON STAFF

SETON PRESS
FRONT ROYAL, VA

Executive Editor: Dr. Mary Kay Clark
Editors: Seton Staff

Printed in the United States of America.

Seton Home Study School
1350 Progress Drive
Front Royal, VA 22630
540-636-9990
540-636-1602 fax

For more information, visit us on the Web at www.setonhome.org
Contact us by e-mail at counselors@setonhome.org

ISBN: 978-1-60704-114-6

Cover: *The Good Shepherd*, Phillipe de Champaigne

Dedicated to the Sacred Heart of Jesus

Jesus, Mary, and Joseph, pray for us.

Spelling 4 for Young Catholics

Contents

NOTES for Parents and teachers

Preface

Seton Home Study School is pleased to present *Spelling 4 for Young Catholics* in our series of Catholic spelling books for Catholic children so that you as a parent-teacher can help your student acquire a solid foundation for correct spelling usage. The spelling exercises in this book will enable your student to complete many spelling exercises independently through continued study and application of spelling rules and word patterns. The spelling word lists are selected from lists of frequently used words as well as lists of frequently misspelled words.

In light of the Vatican's directive for schools to incorporate the Faith throughout the curriculum, Catholic ideas are included in the text. The Bible stories and examples in this book illustrate the rules of spelling, while the oil paintings depict various religious pictures. We hope that this presentation will not only facilitate the learning of the subject at hand, but also supplement the awareness of Biblical history and culture, as well as deepen the knowledge and practice of the Catholic Faith in your student's daily life.

Introduction

Each book in the *Spelling for Young Catholics* series builds upon the concepts taught in previous grades. Through the exercises in the *Spelling 4* lessons, your student will learn to spell multisyllabic words containing regular and irregular spelling patterns. The memorization of frequently occurring words containing irregular spellings will enable your student to spell many words correctly and to apply newly acquired spelling skills to daily writing assignments. Encourage your student to use a dictionary to verify the spelling and meaning of new and different words.

The beginning series of *Spelling 1* and *Spelling 2 for Young Catholics* teach your student how to spell by listening to letter sounds and identifying regular spelling patterns. The focus in *Spelling 3 for Young Catholics* extends to fostering a proficiency in memorizing and spelling frequently used words having irregular spellings. In this book, lessons on unaccented syllables, prefixes, and suffixes are included.

Spelling 4 for Young Catholics continues to teach the spelling of words with different vowel sounds and combinations of letters. In addition, the spelling words include lists of compound words and words with similar prefixes and suffixes. The entire series, *Spelling for Young Catholics*, provides a solid foundation for correct spelling usage. Encourage your student to build upon this foundation with continued study and application of spelling rules and word patterns.

The importance of spelling correctly cannot be overstated. Incorrect spelling results in reading, writing, and general communication problems. Anyone who is struggling to read a letter, report, essay, or anything else with incorrect spelling will soon give up trying to read it. Most employers will quickly discard any job application that contains spelling errors.

Our aim in this book is to help your student master the challenges of spelling correctly. It is important to remember that being a good speller has little to do with being "smart," but rather is a basic *skill* that anyone can master.

Requirements

The weekly lessons in each level of our *Spelling for Young Catholics* series build upon previous lessons from earlier grades. It is a good idea for your student to keep spelling books completed earlier, in order to periodically review the words that have already been covered and, hopefully, learned well.

Your student should be able to spell words with regular spellings by listening to the sounds of the letters and applying spelling rules. Words with irregular spellings, however, must be memorized. These words are called *sight words*, and they do not follow any spelling rules. Identifying sounds in words is an *auditory* (hearing and listening) exercise, while memorizing the spelling of words is a *visual* (seeing) exercise. For some of us, the visual memory is stronger than the auditory memory, so it is important to also use visual aids, such as flash cards, in learning to spell.

Pronunciation

In *Spelling 4*, letter combinations are used as pronunciation symbols. Pronunciation symbols for vowel and consonant sounds vary somewhat among different dictionaries. You may refer your student to the pronunciation symbols used in your dictionary at home.

In trying to achieve spelling mastery, it can be beneficial to exaggerate the pronunciation of unstressed vowels while looking at and reading a word. In doing so, your student will likely associate the pronunciation with the correct spelling of the vowel. The word *Catholic*, for example, technically has three spelling syllables. When pronouncing for correct spelling, the exaggerated three-syllable pronunciation (***Cath-o-lic***) may also be used as a visual memory device along with the auditory one as we look at the written word.

Remind your student that the number of spelling syllables (not pronunciation syllables) in a word is determined by the number of vowel sounds. In daily language, of course, your student should pronounce these words correctly. Only when pronouncing for a spelling memory device should your student pronounce in an exaggerated manner.

Pronunciation Symbols

Below, note how the various sounds are represented by the pronunciation symbols, shown within a pair of slashes, such as /aa/. An example of each sound is provided next to the symbol. It is not necessary for your student to memorize a specific set of pronunciation symbols. What is important is that your student be able to hear the sounds by saying them, and then memorize the spellings that represent each sound.

Short Vowel Sounds	Long Vowel Sounds	Other Vowel Sounds
the /aa/ sound in at	the /ay/ sound in ate	the /aw/ sound in awe
the /eh/ sound in egg	the /ee/ sound in eve	the /oo/ sound in ooze
the /ih/ sound in it	the /iy/ sound in ice	the /uu/ sound in book
the /ah/ sound in ox	the /oh/ sound in oak	the /ou/ sound in out
the /uh/ sound in us	the /yoo/ sound in use	the /oi/ sound in oil

Some dictionaries use different pronunciation symbols for vowels followed by the consonant *r* because the pronunciation of some r-controlled vowels varies among different dialects. In this book, the pronunciation symbol for the vowel sound is combined with the symbol for the sound of *r*. Note this combination in the following symbols for r-controlled vowel sounds:

- the /ar/ sound in ark;
- the /ur/ sound in urn;
- the /ayr/ sound in air;
- the /eer/ sound in ear;
- the /or/ sound in oar.

Using the *Spelling 4* Book

The *Spelling 4* book is intended to be completed in one academic year, which consists of thirty-six weeks, or four quarters. Therefore, there are thirty-six weekly lessons and exercises altogether. Each week is divided into four lessons and a test day. There are exercises to be covered on the first four days of the week and a test to be given on the fifth day. Parents are asked to administer a spelling test on that day. Each quarter within the academic year consists of nine weeks. The last lesson of each quarter provides a quarterly review in preparation for the quarterly test. The quarterly test is administered four times a year, or every nine weeks.

In the back of the book is a list of the Spelling Rules, along with Art Credits listing the titles and artists of the art found throughout the book. An Answer Key to all the exercises in the book is also provided in the back of the book. If you find it helpful, you may tear out the answer key for your use, or you can make a copy of it to help you in correcting the exercises.

Bonus Word

Each word list includes one bonus word. The bonus word may be more difficult than the other words in the list. It is included in the list to exemplify an alternate spelling relating to the lesson. While bonus words are not included on Quarter Tests, your student should study the bonus word along with the other words in the word list. When grading the weekly tests, divide the total number of correct words by 15 rather than 16 total words. In this manner, the bonus word provides the student with bonus points in the weekly test grade. For example, if your student spells all words correctly, including the bonus word, you divide 16 by 15 to calculate a score of 107%. On the other hand, if your student misspells one word, either the bonus word or another word, you divide 15 by 15 to calculate a score of 100%. With this grading strategy, your student will quickly learn the advantage of paying careful attention to the bonus word.

Instructions for Daily Exercises

Day One. This is the most important lesson of the week. Read the spelling rule at the top of the page. Notice that the letters between the slashes, such as /ay/, are pronounced by the sound of the spelling in the sample word. Pronounce the sound of the spelling in the shaded boxes rather than the name of the letters. Notice the application of the rule in each word or some of the spelling words. Pronounce each spelling word, then spell it aloud, then repeat the word.

Exercise A: Sort by Syllable, Sort by Spelling, or Sort by Sound. Complete the exercise, pronouncing all the words from the spelling list. Start with the first word in the list. Not all the exercises on the first page are the same, but usually you must find the spelling of the sound in the exercise that matches the spelling of the sound of words in the word list. Write the list word in the section that corresponds to the spelling or syllables. Check your spelling. Continue this exercise with each additional word on the list. Some of the later exercises are on compound words, prefixes, and suffixes. In some of the later exercises, the words are to be written according to the number of syllables. We are not asking the student to separate the words by syllables, but the Answer Key does show the words separated by syllable, which may help your student to spell the words more easily.

Day Two. Exercise B: Definitions. The exercise for this day is a list of definitions for which the student needs to write one of the list words on the lines at the right. This is an important exercise for writing the spelling words correctly once again, and for understanding the meaning of the words.

Day Three. Exercise C: Missing Words. Write the correct spelling words on the blank lines on the right for the missing words in the sentences. Start with the first sentence. Find the list word that fits in the blank. Write it in the blank. Say the word. Read the complete sentence, and then repeat the word. Each list word may be used only once in this exercise. Try to spell each word without looking at the word list. Check your spelling. If you misspelled the word, erase it and write it correctly. Continue this exercise with each additional sentence.

Optional: After completing this exercise, the words may be dictated into a recorder as a further drill for writing the words. Correct any misspelled words and rewrite them five times each.

Day Four. Exercise D: Story Time. Stories are presented with words underlined which follow the spelling rule for the lesson. In addition, write the words in the spelling list in alphabetical order on a separate sheet of paper.

Day Five. Parents should dictate the list of spelling words for a weekly test. Listen to the words as they are dictated alone and within a sentence. Write each word carefully on a separate sheet of paper. Correct any misspelled words, and rewrite them five times each.

Memorizing Spelling Words

Experts tell us that in order to learn to spell most effectively, it is best to combine the use of three of our senses. We use our auditory sense (hearing) when we pronounce the word or hear it pronounced; we use the visual sense (seeing) when we look at the word and make a mental image of it (memory); and we use the kinesthetic sense (touch) when we physically write the word down on paper. Since identifying the sounds in words phonetically is an auditory (hearing) exercise, while memorizing the spelling of words is a visual (seeing) exercise, we can use visual aids, such as flash cards, in learning to spell. Here are the recommended steps to follow:

1. Write the spelling words on flash cards and then place them on a wall or poster board in front of you so that you will use your eyes, your visual sense.
2. Look at the word long and hard. In your mind, break the word up into syllables, and notice any smaller words within the word.
3. Take a mental snapshot of the word. Blink your eyes like the shutter of a camera and hold them closed for a few seconds. Then spell the word out loud.
4. Test yourself by writing the word on paper. If you made a mistake, repeat the process.
5. To implant the spelling in your memory, say or sing the word out loud, then spell the word out loud as you commit it to memory.

The word should now be solidly in place in your visual, kinesthetic, and auditory memory.

NAME ______________________

In each sentence below, there is a blank corresponding to one of the words found in the word list. Write the missing word in the space next to the sentence.

The butterfly had yellow and ___ wings.	1. ____________
The apostles fished all night but did not ___ any fish.	2. ____________
It was by ___ that I met Father Smith at the library.	3. ____________
I jump rope during my gym ___.	4. ____________
She learned how to ___ at the festival by following along with the Irish dancers.	5. ____________
Many ___ were involved in her decision.	6. ____________
Please refill my ___ with lemonade.	7. ____________
The altar boy mowed the ___ in the churchyard.	8. ____________
Johnny's blue eyes ___ his sister's.	9. ____________
The car ___ the slow truck.	10. ____________
She is not sure but ___ she will go to Confession tomorrow.	11. ____________
We do not know how many ___ God created in outer space.	12. ____________
Mom put the Easter lily ___ in front of the altar.	13. ____________
The choir needed to ___ during Mass.	14. ____________
The ten horses raced around the race ___.	15. ____________
Dad showed me how to make a ___ with my ruler.	16. ____________

NAME ______________________

D Story Time

Read the following story, paying attention to the underlined words. Notice how they use the spelling rule to the right.

The **/aa/** sound in **a**t is usually spelled **a**.

Creation

God created the heavens and the earth according to an orderly plan. First, He made the world. Then He filled it with the things that would be needed later by the creatures He was going to make. He made every plant after He had created the light, air, and water that was needed. The vegetable world was to be food and shelter for the animal world. When all was ready, He created the fish and the birds, the cattle and the wild beasts.

Nothing ever happens by chance, and nothing in God's creation is ever forgotten. God says Himself that all He has created is good. How could it be any different? God is Infinite Goodness. In addition, His creatures are a way of showing His glory and goodness to mankind. Through His creatures, we can come to love God more than ever.

GOD CREATED THE HEAVENS AND THE EARTH.

Adam and Eve lived in the Garden of Paradise.

Jesus, Mary, Joseph, I love You. Save souls!

J.M.J.

NAME ______________________________

LESSON 2

/eh/ sound in egg

smell ✓
desert ✓
fresh ✓
spell ✓
whether ✗
cells
guess ✓
cents
death
sense
friends
ready
weather
dress
check

BONUS

length

The /**eh**/ sound in **e**gg is usually spelled **e** or **ea**.
Sight words have unusual spellings.

A Sort by Syllable

Each box below has a different spelling of the **/eh/** sound in egg. On each line, write a list word that has the same spelling of this sound as the one in the box.

e	smell
	desert
	fresh
	spell
	whether
	cells
	guess
	cents
	dress ✗
	sense
	friends
ea	ready
	weather
	death
sight words	friends
	length

NAME ________________________________

B Definitions

Below are given definitions to the words found in the list. Write the appropriate word in the space provided next to the definition.

very small rooms	1. ______________
pennies	2. ______________
to make sure that something is correct	3. ______________
the end of physical life	4. ______________
girls' or ladies' garment	5. ______________
newly made; not stale or spoiled	6. ______________
people who like each other	7. ______________
prepared	8. ______________
to judge without sure knowledge	9. ______________
a measured distance	10. ______________
special function of the body: taste, smell, sight	11. ______________
odor, scent	12. ______________
to name the letters of a word in correct order	13. ______________
a dry barren region	14. ______________
used to introduce one choice or possibility	15. ______________
the state of the air and atmosphere	16. ______________

NAME ______________________________

In each sentence below, there is a blank corresponding to one of the words found in the word list. Write the missing word in the space next to the sentence.

The May Queen was not ___ for the procession.	1. ____________
The nuns slept in little rooms called ___.	2. ____________
Bananas cost thirty-nine ___ a pound.	3. ____________
Father would ___ the Gospel before Mass.	4. ____________
My good grandfather did not fear ___.	5. ____________
Jesus prayed in the ___ for forty days.	6. ____________
Miriam wore a fancy ___ to the party.	7. ____________
He delivered baskets of ___ flowers for the wedding.	8. ____________
Mary could not ___ which rosary belonged to her.	9. ____________
He did not like rainy ___.	10. ____________
Did you misjudge the ___ of the trip?	11. ____________
Grandmother had lost her ___ of taste.	12. ____________
The great cathedral was filled with the ___ of incense.	13. ____________
Please repeat the word after you ___ it.	14. ____________
It is unclear ___ rain caused the accident.	15. ____________
Many of Mom's ___ came to the Baptism.	16. ____________

NAME ______________________

D Story Time

Read the following story, paying attention to the underlined words. Notice how they use the spelling rule to the right.

The **/eh/** sound in **e**gg is usually spelled **e** or **ea**.

Adam and Eve

God created the world in six days. Man is the last work of God's creation. The world and all the things in it were made for man. First, God made angels in His image and likeness. They are spirits. They can think, reason, and choose to do things. Then God made another creature in His image, man. Man is composed of both soul and body.

Adam was the first man. He had a pleasant life taking care of the Garden of Paradise, which was his home. Neither cold nor hot, the weather in the Garden was always perfect. He saw all the animals, and he gave them all names. But none of them could talk and laugh with him. God saw that Adam was lonely, so He put him in a deep sleep, and taking one of his ribs, God made Eve. Eve became Adam's wife, and they lived together in the Garden. As long as they obeyed God's rules, they would never experience death.

LESSON

3

/ih/ sound in it

history
inches
killed
rhythm
similar
since
sister
built
stick
still
symbols
system
thick
village
which

BONUS

winter

NAME ______________________________

The **/ih/** sound in **i**t is usually spelled **i**, **y**, or **ui**.

A Sort by Syllable

Each box below has a different spelling of the /ih/ sound in it. On each line, write a list word that has the same spelling of this sound as the one in the box.

i	history
	inches
	killed
	similar
	since
	sister
	stick
	still
	thick
	village
	which
	winter
ui	buiAt
y	rhythm
	system
	system

NAME

B Definitions

Below are given definitions to the words found in the list. Write the appropriate word in the space provided next to the definition.

Definition	Answer
deprived of life	1. killed
made by putting parts together	2. build
from a definite past time until now	3. since
cut or broken branch	4. stick
quiet; without sound or motion	5. still
bulky; opposite of thin	6. thick
units of length equal to one-twelfth of a foot	7. inches
a girl having a parent in common with another	8. sister
a telling of past events	9. history
a place smaller than a town	10. village
a word used in place of the name of something	11. which
having qualities in common; alike	12. simular
regular accented beats in music	13. rhymthm
signs; marks representing something else	14. symble
plan; arrangement; method	15. system
the season between autumn and spring	16. winter

J.M.J.

Jesus, Mary, Joseph, I love You. Save souls!

NAME ____________________

In each sentence below, there is a blank corresponding to one of the words found in the word list. Write the missing word in the space next to the sentence.

St. Joseph ___ a sturdy bench for the table.	1. ________
My father wrote a ___ about the war.	2. ________
The pants were three ___ too long for Tim.	3. ________
Many knights were ___ in the Crusades.	4. ________
Dominic loved to beat out the ___ on his drums.	5. ________
The twin sisters liked to wear ___ clothes.	6. ________
Ever ___ Brendan and Susan got married, they have been very happy.	7. ________
My ___ is the oldest girl in the family.	8. ________
It is dangerous to play with a sharp ___.	9. ________
The children sat very ___ as Father told the Bible story.	10. ________
The flag is just one of several national American ___.	11. ________
Mom taught us a ___ for cleaning the kitchen.	12. ________
I like ___ and crispy waffles.	13. ________
Our town has grown from a small ___ to a large city.	14. ________
___ is your favorite passage in the Bible?	15. ________
We will be storing our ___ clothes in the attic during summer.	16. ________

NAME

D Story Time

Read the following story, paying attention to the underlined words. Notice how they use the spelling rule to the right.

The /**ih**/ sound in **i**t is usually spelled **i**, **y**, or **ui**.

The Fall and the Promise

Adam and Eve were disobedient to God and ate the fruit from the Tree of Knowledge of Good and Evil. Their sin is called the Fall of Man, because it took man from the state of grace, which he had enjoyed before. The effect of this sin reaches every man ever born. It was this sin that brought pain and sorrow, shame and suffering to each man.

Sometimes people wonder if God is just for making the whole world suffer for Adam's guilt. This question is asked only by those who do not understand our relationship with God. God made a contract with Adam. If he would obey God and love Him in all things, he and his children would receive eternal life in Heaven. Adam failed to obey, and the contract was broken.

Even though Adam disobeyed God, God still loved him. That is why God promised a Redeemer. Because it is through a woman that man came to sin, through a woman, man would be saved. Her son would conquer sin forever and allow man to enter Heaven. This was achieved by the Son of Mary, Jesus Christ.

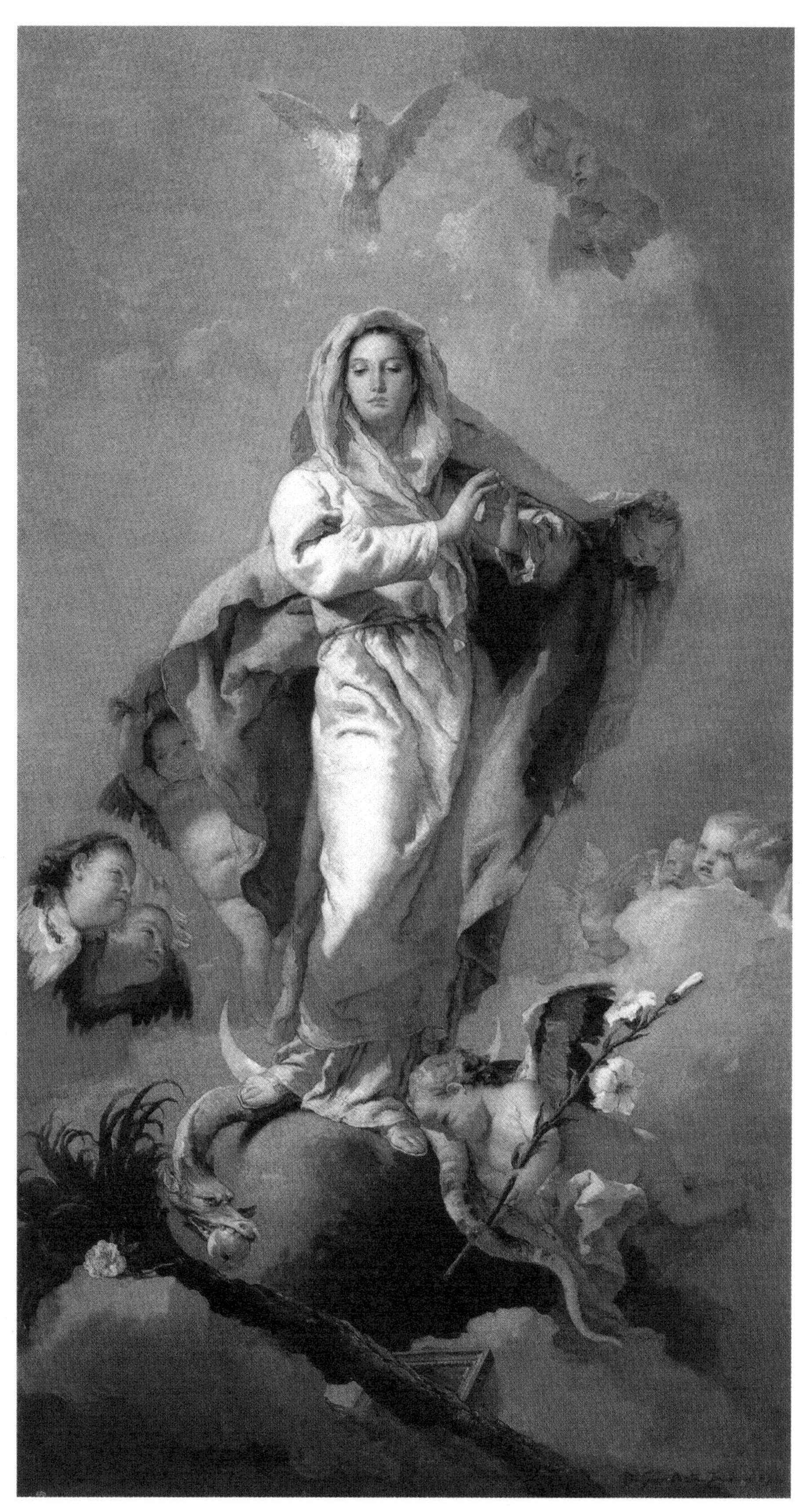

Mary, Queen of Heaven and Earth

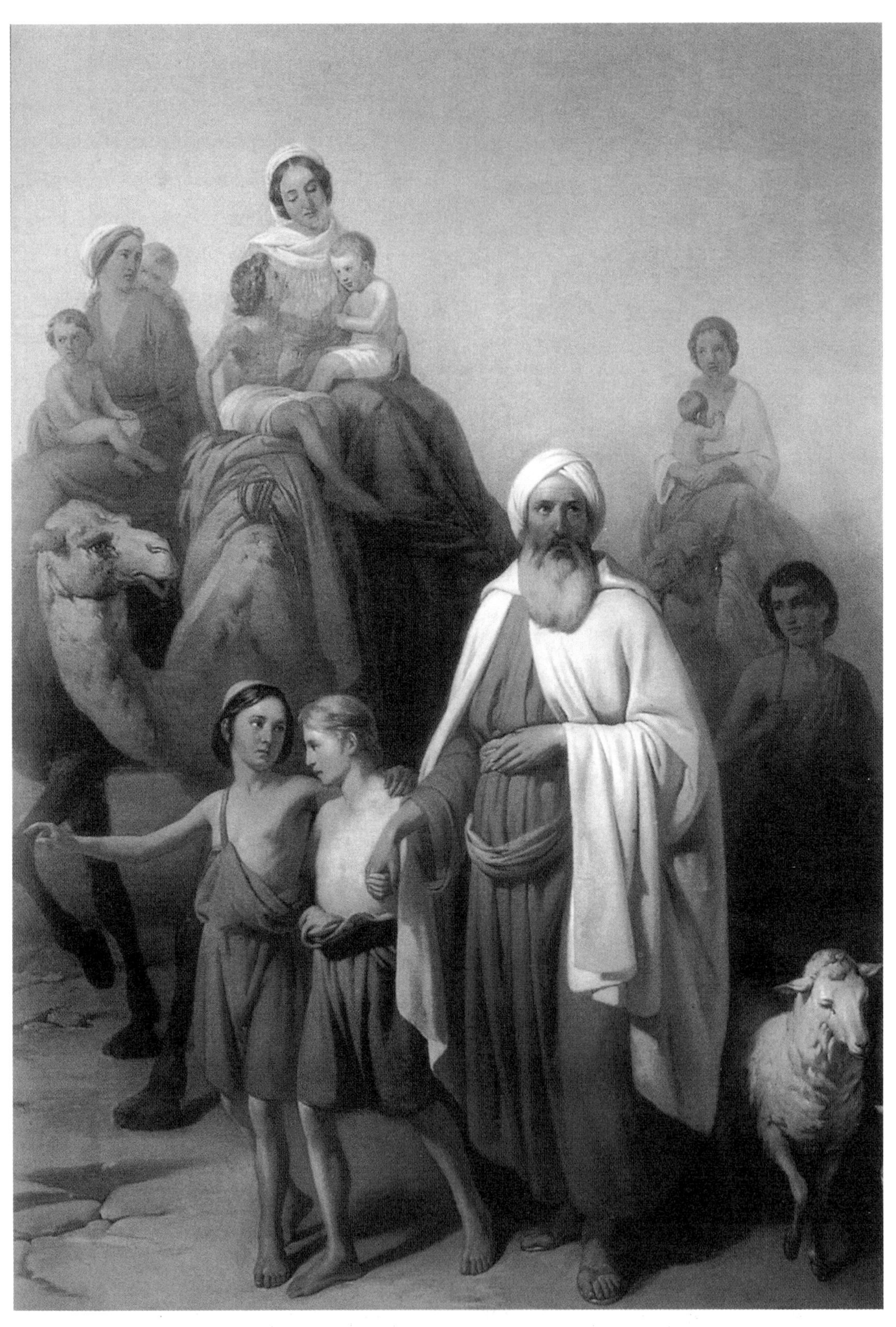

Abraham departs for Canaan.

NAME ____________________

LESSON 4

/ah/ sound in ox

possible
bottom
property
topic
probable
cotton
promise
crops
dollars
products
modern
block
opposite
common
problem

BONUS

column

The **/ah/** sound in **o**x is usually spelled **o** (**o**dd).

A Sort by Syllable

Sort and write the words by the number of syllables.

1	____________________ ____________________
2	____________________ ____________________ ____________________ ____________________ ____________________ ____________________ ____________________ ____________________ ____________________ ____________________
3	____________________ ____________________ ____________________ ____________________

NAME ____________________

B Definitions

Below are given definitions to the words found in the list. Write the appropriate word in the space provided next to the definition.

Definition	
to stop or prevent passage; a solid piece of material with flat sides	1. ____________
fruits or grains grown on a farm for harvesting	2. ____________
the under surface of something	3. ____________
paper money, each equal to 100 cents	4. ____________
something to be solved	5. ____________
something that is owned	6. ____________
articles; things produced	7. ____________
very likely	8. ____________
relating to the present time	9. ____________
something completely different from another	10. ____________
vertical support; pillar	11. ____________
ordinary	12. ____________
soft fluffy material	13. ____________
that could happen or exist	14. ____________
the subject of a speech or writing	15. ____________
a pledge to do something	16. ____________

NAME ____________________

In each sentence below, there is a blank corresponding to one of the words found in the word list. Write the missing word in the space next to the sentence.

Father asked the children not to ___ the church entrance.	1. ____________
The thread came out of the ___ hem of the altar vestment.	2. ____________
Flowered vines grew up beside each large white ___ in front of the church.	3. ____________
The doctor said Suzie had the ___ cold.	4. ____________
Sometimes clouds resemble fluffy balls of ___.	5. ____________
A plague of locusts destroyed the ___ of the Egyptians.	6. ____________
We will be exchanging ___ for quarters and dimes.	7. ____________
The ___ heating system keeps the house much warmer than our old radiator.	8. ____________
Dan could not solve the math ___ in his lesson.	9. ____________
Most cleaning ___ are dangerous poisons.	10. ____________
My aunt made a ___ to take me to the shrine on Sunday.	11. ____________
The nuns' convent was located on the ___ side of the street from the church.	12. ____________
Because she was sick, it was not ___ for Jane to attend the meeting.	13. ____________
Our pastor said it was very ___ that he would go on the hike with the altar boys.	14. ____________
Damaging someone's ___ is a sin against the seventh commandment.	15. ____________
Mary's beautiful wedding was the ___ of conversation for a few weeks.	16. ____________

NAME ____________________

D Story Time

Read the following story, paying attention to the underlined words. Notice how they use the spelling rule to the right.

The **/ah/** sound in **o**x is usually spelled **o** (**o**dd).

Abraham Goes to Canaan

Abram was a herder living near the city of Ur. While most men had forgotten about the one true God, Abram was still faithful to Him. One day, Abram and his wife, his father and his nephew Lot set out from Ur to go to a land called Canaan, but when they came to the city of Haran, they stopped there. There Abram's father, who was old and feeble, died after a long life, and Abram buried him.

Then God spoke to Abram, telling him to take his family and possessions and go to the land that would be shown to him. Abram was obedient and did what God asked. He continued on his journey, with his flocks of sheep and Lot's family, to find the place God wanted to show him.

This time, Abram was moving southwest past spots of desert land. Soon he came to a land called Canaan. It ran along the coast of the Mediterranean Sea. There were hills and valleys, grasslands and arbors. This is the land that God gave to Abram and his descendants. When Abram was ninety-nine years old, God changed his name to Abraham, which means, "Ancestor of many nations."

NAME ______________________

LESSON 5

/uh/ sound in us

suffix

jumped

hundred

judge

funny

months

truck

color

southern

front

minutes

money

summer

touch

subject

BONUS

blood

The **/uh/** sound in **u**s is spelled **u** (**u**p), **ou** (t**ou**ch), or **o** (m**o**nths).

A Sort by Syllable

Each box below has a different spelling of the /**uh**/ sound in **u**s. On each line, write a list word that has the same spelling of this sound as the one in the box.

o	______________
	______________
	______________
	______________
ou	______________
	______________
u	______________
	______________
	______________
	______________
	______________
	______________
	______________
	______________
sight word	______________

NAME ____________________

B Definitions

Below are given definitions to the words found in the list. Write the appropriate word in the space provided next to the definition.

a vehicle for carrying heavy articles	1. ________
the forward part of something	2. ________
leaped	3. ________
12 parts of the year	4. ________
word part that comes at the end of a word, changing the meaning, such as -ed, -ing	5. ________
like that of the south	6. ________
parts of an hour, each 60 seconds	7. ________
hue or appearance of a thing	8. ________
a course of study; topic of a sentence	9. ________
to feel or handle; physical contact	10. ________
red fluid that circulates in the body	11. ________
season between spring and autumn	12. ________
ten times ten	13. ________
causing laughter	14. ________
the coins or paper notes of a country used to buy things and pay for services	15. ________
an official who decides questions in a court of law; to give an opinion of	16. ________

NAME ____________________

In each sentence below, there is a blank corresponding to one of the words found in the word list. Write the missing word in the space next to the sentence.

There are sixty ___ in an hour.	1. ____________
St. Paul warns us that the love of ___ is the root of all evil.	2. ____________
Jesus says we must not ___ others, lest we be judged.	3. ____________
St. Veronica wiped the ___ from the face of Jesus.	4. ____________
The ___ of Dad's tie matched his shirt.	5. ____________
He met her in ___ of the store.	6. ____________
Joseph told a ___ joke.	7. ____________
There must have been a ___ apples in the bushel basket.	8. ____________
The dog ___ high to catch the ball.	9. ____________
It took ___ for our house to be built.	10. ____________
We took the ___ route rather than the eastern route.	11. ____________
My favorite ___ to study is spelling.	12. ____________
The ___ in the word "jumped" is *ed*.	13. ____________
Last ___ was hotter than this one.	14. ____________
The sick woman tried to ___ the cloak of Jesus.	15. ____________
Dad rented a ___ to move our furniture.	16. ____________

NAME

D Story Time

Read the following story, paying attention to the underlined words. Notice how they use the spelling rule to the right.

The **/uh/** sound in **u**s is spelled **u** (**u**p), **ou** (t**ou**ch), or **o** (m**o**nths).

Lot and Abraham

Because Abraham's and Lot's hired men were engaged in much quarreling, Abraham gave Lot the land to the east of his own settlement, to end such conflicts. Lot moved with his family near the city of Sodom.

It happened that a battle was fought near this city, and Sodom's enemy won. The cities of Sodom and Gomorrah were sacked, and Lot's family was taken prisoner.

A soldier escaped during the battle and told Abraham what had happened. So Abraham gathered some of his men, and his neighbor gathered some of his men. Together they followed the enemy, and suddenly ambushed his camp. The enemy was defeated, and Lot's family was rescued. Together, they set off to return home.

On the way, they stopped near the town of Salem. Men from this town came to the valley where Abraham set up his camp. Among them was the king of Salem. His name was Melchisedek, and he was also a priest. He believed in the true God of Abraham. This priest offered a sacrifice of bread and wine to God in thanksgiving for the safe return of the captives.

Abraham meets Melchisedek.

Jacob tricks Isaac into blessing him.

NAME ____________________

LESSON 6

/ay/ sound in ate

shape
place
strange
plains
weight
raised
state
waves
paint
space
plane
straight
trade
phrase
train

BONUS

scale

The **/ay/** sound in **a**te is spelled **a** (usually followed by a silent e, as in **a**ge), **ai** (**ai**d), or **eigh** (**eigh**t).

A Sort by Syllable

Each box below has a different spelling of the /**ay**/ sound in **a**te. On each line, write a list word that has the same spelling of this sound as the one in the box.

a	____________________
	____________________
	____________________
	____________________
	____________________
	____________________
	____________________
	____________________
	____________________
	____________________
ai	____________________
	____________________
	____________________
	____________________
	____________________
eigh	____________________

NAME ______________________________

B Definitions

Below are given definitions to the words found in the list. Write the appropriate word in the space provided next to the definition.

a mixture of coloring matter with a liquid	1. ________
a brief expression using words	2. ________
location; to put	3. ________
large area of level treeless land	4. ________
airplane	5. ________
lifted	6. ________
instrument for weighing	7. ________
outward appearance, such as circle or square	8. ________
an empty place	9. ________
one of the 50 divisions of the U.S.	10. ________
not having curves	11. ________
unfamiliar; odd	12. ________
to give in exchange for something else	13. ________
connected railway cars	14. ________
rolling movements such as on the surface of water	15. ________
the amount that something weighs	16. ________

NAME ______________________________

C Missing Words

In each sentence below, there is a blank corresponding to one of the words found in the word list. Write the missing word in the space next to the sentence.

The ___ will depart shortly from the airport.	1. ____________
To the onlookers' great surprise, Jesus ___ Lazarus from the dead.	2. ____________
My dad stood on the ___ to see his weight.	3. ____________
The clay conformed to the ___ of the mold.	4. ____________
The walls of this room will need two coats of ___.	5. ____________
An adjective ___ describes a noun.	6. ____________
California seems to be the likeliest ___ for earthquakes.	7. ____________
Early Catholic pioneers left cities to settle in the Great ___.	8. ____________
We like to ___ our holy cards with other kids.	9. ____________
As the storm raged, angry ___ beat against the boat of the apostles.	10. ____________
We were surprised at the heavy ___ of the new picture Bible.	11. ____________
Five boxcars of the ___ derailed off the track.	12. ____________
Our bunk beds do not take up much ___.	13. ____________
My grandfather lives in the ___ of Alabama.	14. ____________
Dad showed me how to draw a ___ line with a ruler.	15. ____________
Kevin saw a fish in the lake with ___ colors.	16. ____________

NAME ______________________________

D Story Time

Read the following story, paying attention to the underlined words. Notice how they use the spelling rule to the right.

The **/ay/** sound in **a**te is spelled **a** (**a**ge), **ai** (**ai**d), or **eigh** (**eigh**t).

The Hebrew Patriarchs

Abraham had no son. Yet God had promised him that he would have many descendants. It was not until both he and his wife were very old that God gave him a son. His name was Isaac.

Isaac became the father of twins, Esau and Jacob. Esau was born first, so he would receive the special favors of the firstborn son. But Jacob wanted these fine honors for himself. He tricked Esau into selling him his birthright. Later, Jacob tricked his father into giving him the blessing which he was saving for the firstborn son.

Because Jacob was wrong in using trickery to get what he wanted, God punished him. First he had to leave his home because Esau wanted to kill him. Then he was fooled by the father of the girl he wanted to marry. He was tricked into marrying her sister first, and could only marry Rachel, the one he loved, later. It was twenty years before he could return home. Esau had forgiven Jacob by this time, and the brothers lived peacefully as neighbors.

One of Jacob's sons was Judah. His mother was Lea, Jacob's first wife. Through Judah's family, Christ would come to us to be our Savior.

NAME ______________________________

LESSON 7

/ee/ sound in eve

sleep
green
stream
leave
wheels
speak
seeds
clean
steel
piece
street
chief
three
field
least

BONUS

speed

The /**ee**/ sound in **e**ve is often spelled **ea** (**ea**se), **ee** (**ee**l), or **ie** (pr**ie**st).

A Sort by Syllable

Each box below has a different spelling of the /**ee**/ sound in **e**ve. On each line, write a list word that has the same spelling of this sound as the one in the box.

ea	______________________________ ______________________________ ______________________________ ______________________________ ______________________________
ee	______________________________ ______________________________ ______________________________ ______________________________ ______________________________ ______________________________ ______________________________ ______________________________
ie	______________________________ ______________________________ ______________________________

NAME ______________________________

B Definitions

Below are given definitions to the words found in the list. Write the appropriate word in the space provided next to the definition.

the head of a group	1. ________
to free of dirt	2. ________
a piece of open land	3. ________
a color seen on lawn grass	4. ________
smallest in size	5. ________
to go away from	6. ________
a part of a thing	7. ________
things plants make that grow into new plants	8. ________
a natural rest at night	9. ________
to talk	10. ________
quickness in action	11. ________
hard metal made by heating iron	12. ________
moving water larger than a brook	13. ________
public road, usually paved for cars	14. ________
the counting number immediately following two	15. ________
circular frames that rotate	16. ________

NAME ______________________________

C Missing Words

In each sentence below, there is a blank corresponding to one of the words found in the word list. Write the missing word in the space next to the sentence.

Jacinta received the ___ amount of candy, but she did not complain.	1. ______________
We must not ___ Mass before it is over.	2. ______________
Who finished the last ___ of cake?	3. ______________
Jesus told a story about ___ planted in rocky ground.	4. ______________
The Indian ___ rode his horse bareback.	5. ______________
Each time I ___ my room, my baby brother messes it up again.	6. ______________
We could not play until the baseball ___ dried up.	7. ______________
In the spring, the grass in Our Lady's grotto becomes bright ___.	8. ______________
The monastery window faced the flowing ___.	9. ______________
We parked our car on the next ___.	10. ______________
We staged a play about the ___ Wise Men.	11. ______________
The ___ on my bicycle are flat.	12. ______________
Lack of ___ will make you tired the next day.	13. ______________
Zachary could not ___ because he did not believe the angel.	14. ______________
Young John, running with great ___, reached the empty tomb first.	15. ______________
The blade of the sword was made of ___.	16. ______________

NAME

D Story Time

Read the following story, paying attention to the underlined words. Notice how they use the spelling rule to the right.

The /**ee**/ sound in **e**ve is often spelled **ea**, **ee**, or **ie**.

The Jews Go to Egypt

Jacob, now called Israel, treated Joseph as his favorite son. His brothers envied Joseph. When they had the opportunity, they sold him to slave traders, who took him to Egypt. There, Joseph was sold to a rich man. After a while, he was sent to prison for a crime he did not commit.

While he was in prison, Joseph met the butler and the baker from the pharaoh's palace. Both had strange dreams, which Joseph interpreted for them. Both of his interpretations came about as he had foreseen. Later the pharaoh had strange dreams also. The butler told the pharaoh about Joseph. The pharaoh requested that Joseph be brought to him.

Joseph came and interpreted his dreams. He told the pharaoh that there would be seven years of plenty, followed by seven years of famine. The pharaoh believed Joseph and put him in charge of gathering and storing the food saved during the first seven years so that no one would starve when the famine came.

Thus it was that Egypt alone had food enough when the famine struck. So everyone in the surrounding area came to them to buy food. Joseph's family did the same. When they found that he was still alive, the whole family moved to Egypt to be near him.

JOSEPH IS PUT IN CHARGE OF EGYPT.

ABRAHAM PREPARES TO SACRIFICE HIS SON, ISAAC.

NAME ______________________________

LESSON 8

/iy/ sound in ice

white
sign
drive
dye
entire
silent
fight
island
provide
design
climbed
describe
disguise
supply
bright

BONUS

child

The **/iy/** sound in **i**ce is spelled **i** (**I**), **igh** (h**igh**), **y** (m**y**), or **ui** (g**ui**de).

A Sort by Syllable

Each box below has a different spelling of the **/iy/** sound in **i**ce. On each line, write a list word that has the same spelling of this sound as the one in the box.

i	______________________
	______________________
	______________________
	______________________
	______________________
	______________________
	______________________
	______________________
	______________________
	______________________
	______________________
igh	______________________
	______________________
ui	______________________
y	______________________
	______________________

NAME ______________________________

B Definitions

Below are given definitions to the words found in the list. Write the appropriate word in the space provided next to the definition.

filled with much light	1. __________
a young person	2. __________
to have gone up, as on stairs	3. __________
to cause to move; to propel	4. __________
a substance used to color material	5. __________
a meeting in battle or combat	6. __________
completely; actually; very	7. __________
a plan; a sketch; a drawing	8. __________
the color of fresh snow	9. __________
a public notice that advertises something	10. __________
not speaking; quiet	11. __________
an area of land surrounded by water	12. __________
to give something that is needed	13. __________
to tell about	14. __________
complete	15. __________
to provide for	16. __________

J.M.J.

Jesus, Mary, Joseph, I love You. Save souls!

NAME ______________________

In each sentence below, there is a blank corresponding to one of the words found in the word list. Write the missing word in the space next to the sentence.

___ light causes my eyes to hurt.	1. ______
Jesus was only a ___ of twelve when He taught the priests.	2. ______
Zacheus ___ into a tree to see Jesus in the crowd.	3. ______
It is difficult to ___ the full beauty of a red sunset!	4. ______
Mom sewed a beautiful red ___ of the Cross on Father's vestment.	5. ______
St. Patrick was known to ___ the snakes out of Ireland.	6. ______
The blue ___ made a beautiful Easter egg.	7. ______
Jesus made the ___ herd of pigs jump off the cliff.	8. ______
The Fifth Commandment forbids us to ___ without a very good reason.	9. ______
St. Paul went from island to ___ working miracles after the shipwreck.	10. ______
We trust that Jesus will ___ and supply everything we need.	11. ______
The spy wore a ___ to enter the enemy camp.	12. ______
The ___ on the store window says there is a sale today!	13. ______
The little girl remained ___ while the priest spoke.	14. ______
Did the people provide enough food for the church to ___ the soup kitchen with bread and soup?	15. ______
Mary Magdalen saw two angels in ___ sitting on His tomb.	16. ______

NAME ______________________________

D Story Time

Read the following story, paying attention to the underlined words. Notice how they use the spelling rule to the right.

The **/iy/** sound in **i**ce is spelled **i** (**I**), **igh** (h**igh**), **y** (m**y**), or **ui** (g**ui**de).

Sacrifice

Sacrifices were offered to God throughout the Old Testament. The best animals were killed and burned to thank God for His blessings.

Abel offered his best lamb to God because of his love for God. God accepted his sacrifice. Abel's brother Cain did not want to offer his best sacrifice. Cain wanted to deny God his complete love, which is why God did not accept his sacrifice. In anger, Cain attacked Abel and killed him. God heard Abel's cry for justice, and He banished Cain.

Abraham also offered sacrifices to God. To test Abraham's love, God asked him to sacrifice his only son Isaac. Abraham gave a deep sigh because he loved Isaac very much. Nevertheless, Abraham took his son up on a high mountainside. He laid Isaac on a pile of branches and tied him with ropes around his arms and thighs. Abraham held his knife high to strike, but God sent an angel to carefully guide Abraham's hand to stop him. God did not allow Abraham to kill his only son, but He saw how much Abraham loved Him. By the example of Abel and Abraham, we can see that we should love God so much that we are willing to offer Him our best gifts.

NAME

Lesson Review

Lesson 1	Lesson 2	Lesson 3	Lesson 4
catch	smell	history	possible
factors	desert	inches	bottom
graph	fresh	killed	property
black	spell	rhythm	topic
grass	whether	similar	probable
passed	cells	since	cotton
class	guess	sister	promise
track	cents	built	crops
perhaps	death	stick	dollars
glass	sense	still	products
dance	friends	symbols	modern
planets	ready	system	block
stand	weather	thick	opposite
chance	dress	village	common
plant	check	which	problem
BONUS	BONUS	BONUS	BONUS
match	length	winter	column

NAME

Tips from your *Guardian Angel*

- Pronounce each word for correct spelling.
- Say the word, spell it, and say it again.
- Divide each word into syllables.
- Take an oral pretest of all these words, then write each misspelled word three times.

Lesson 5	Lesson 6	Lesson 7	Lesson 8
suffix	shape	sleep	white
jumped	place	green	sign
hundred	strange	stream	drive
judge	plains	leave	dye
funny	weight	wheels	entire
months	raised	speak	silent
truck	state	seeds	fight
color	waves	clean	island
southern	paint	steel	provide
front	space	piece	design
minutes	plane	street	climbed
money	straight	chief	describe
summer	trade	three	quite
touch	phrase	field	supply
subject	train	least	bright
BONUS	BONUS	BONUS	BONUS
blood	scale	speed	child

J.M.J.

NAME ____________________

LESSON 10

/oh/ sound in oak

folded
control
stone
known
soldiers
police
shoulder
bones
rolled
slowly
clothes
although
suppose
hello
coast

BONUS

shown

The **/oh/** sound in **oa**k is spelled **o** (**o**de), **ow** (**ow**n), **ough** (d**ough**), **oa** (**oa**k), or **ou** (b**ou**lder).

A Sort by Syllable

Each box below has a different spelling of the /**oh**/ sound in **oa**k. On each line, write a list word that has the same spelling of this sound as the one in the box.

o	____________________
	____________________
	____________________
	____________________
	____________________
	____________________
	____________________
	____________________
	____________________
	____________________
oa	____________________
ou	____________________
ough	____________________
ow	____________________
	____________________
	____________________

NAME ____________________

B Definitions

Below are given definitions to the words found in the list. Write the appropriate word in the space provided next to the definition.

the hard material of the skeleton	1. ________
clothing; garments	2. ________
the land near a shore	3. ________
people who keep order and enforce the law	4. ________
to believe; to think of as true	5. ________
understood	6. ________
turned over and over on a surface	7. ________
displayed	8. ________
rock	9. ________
bent over upon itself so that one section lies on or against another section	10. ________
persons in military service	11. ________
gradually; without haste	12. ________
a greeting	13. ________
in spite of the fact that	14. ________
the part of the body where the arm joins the body	15. ________
to have power over	16. ________

NAME ______________________

In each sentence below, there is a blank corresponding to one of the words found in the word list. Write the missing word in the space next to the sentence.

___ it seems unbelievable, a huge fish really did swallow Jonas.	1. ________
Drinking milk will give us strong ___.	2. ________
Grandpa's sore ___ hurts when it rains.	3. ________
Store your winter ___ in the attic during the summer.	4. ________
My friend said there are sharks off the west ___ of Australia.	5. ________
The Fifth Commandment commands us to ___ our anger.	6. ________
St. Anthony is ___ as the Finder of Lost Things.	7. ________
Jim's marbles ___ all over the floor.	8. ________
Veronica had not yet ___ her new puppy to her friend.	9. ________
A granite stepping ___ led into the private garden.	10. ________
They say the burial cloth of Christ was ___ into four equal sections.	11. ________
The battle wore on, but the weary ___ remained undefeated.	12. ________
The nurse said to breathe deeply and ___.	13. ________
Always say ___ when you answer the phone.	14. ________
The ___ are always ready to help people in trouble.	15. ________
You cannot ___ that to be true; you need to prove it.	16. ________

NAME

D Story Time

Read the following story, paying attention to the underlined words. Notice how they use the spelling rule to the right.

The **/oh/** sound in **oa**k is spelled **o**, **ow**, **ough**, **oa**, or **ou**.

Enslaving the Jews

When the Jews moved to Egypt, they settled in a part of that land called Goshen. There they raised their cattle and had little to do with the civilized but pagan Egyptians. God blessed them, and their families grew. The Israelites started spreading over other parts of the country, learning other skills, including how to farm and trade, and gaining knowledge of the culture and its government.

After Pharaoh, the friend of Joseph, had died, new pharaohs came to the throne. They soon realized that the Israelites were strong enough to fight on the side of the enemy if they were attacked. They eliminated this threat by enslaving them, forcing them to work hard with little food. The Egyptians treated the Israelites very cruelly. But God took care of His people, and they continued to multiply. So the pharaoh decided that every baby boy born to the Israelites was to be thrown into the Nile River.

This pagan nation was treating the children of God very cruelly. It was for this reason that God saved Moses from death, that he might lead the people of God back to their homeland.

Moses is saved from death.

The Ark is carried in a procession.

NAME ______________________________

LESSON 11

/aw/ sound in awe

outlaw
all right
cause
naughty
oftentimes
brought
caught
autumn
bought
cross
drawing
office
across
chalk
small

BONUS

already

The **/aw/** sound in **aw**e is spelled **a** (**a**ll), **o** (**o**ff), **aw** (**aw**e), **au** (P**au**l), **augh** (n**augh**ty), or **ough** (b**ough**t).

A Sort by Syllable

Each box below has a different spelling of the /**aw**/ sound in **aw**e. On each line, write a list word that has the same spelling of this sound as the one in the box.

a	______________________
	______________________
	______________________
	______________________
au	______________________
	______________________
augh	______________________
	______________________
aw	______________________
	______________________
o	______________________
	______________________
	______________________
	______________________
ough	______________________
	______________________

NAME ______________________________

B Definitions

Below are given definitions to the words found in the list. Write the appropriate word in the space provided next to the definition.

purchased	1. ________
caused to come; carried	2. ________
a thing that brings about a result	3. ________
sketching	4. ________
from one side to the other side	5. ________
satisfactory	6. ________
many times	7. ________
guilty of disobedience or other bad behavior	8. ________
someone who runs away from the law	9. ________
the season between summer and winter	10. ________
a structure of one bar crossing another at right angles	11. ________
a place where business is done	12. ________
little in size	13. ________
before a certain time; previously	14. ________
captured something in motion	15. ________
soft, usually white, limestone used to write or draw	16. ________

NAME ____________________

In each sentence below, there is a blank corresponding to one of the words found in the word list. Write the missing word in the space next to the sentence.

Mother said the younger children are not allowed to go ___ the street by themselves.	1. ________
I have ___ received my first Holy Communion.	2. ________
Dad said it is ___ for me to go with him to Florida.	3. ________
My sister painted an ___ scene of orange and yellow trees.	4. ________
Mom gives my little brother a spanking when he is ___.	5. ________
Grandma ___ the green paint at the paint store.	6. ________
Thankfully, the fire alarm ___ everyone out of the building.	7. ________
Thomas ___ the ball with his baseball glove.	8. ________
The researcher discovered the ___ of the disease.	9. ________
Mother likes us to diagram on the blackboard using ___.	10. ________
Jesus died on the ___ to open the gates of Heaven.	11. ________
Ben became a famous artist because of his ___ skills.	12. ________
The sheriff caught up with the ___.	13. ________
Drop off the keys for the car at Dad's ___.	14. ________
The ___ boat could not navigate in the starless night.	15. ________
___ I attend Mass at the Shrine of St. Mary.	16. ________

NAME ______________________

D Story Time

Read the following story, paying attention to the underlined words. Notice how they use the spelling rule to the right.

The **/aw/** sound in **aw**e is spelled **a**, **o**, **aw**, **au**, **augh**, or **ough**.

The Ark and the Tabernacle

By working many miracles, God, through Moses, led the Israelites out of Egypt, and they started their journey <u>across</u> the desert back to the Promised Land. Even though they knew that it was God leading them back to their home, the people wanted an image of God that they could see. God knew they needed an object to remind them of Him and His <u>Laws</u>. So God showed Moses how to make a chest, called the Ark of the Covenant, to hold the tablets of stone upon which the Ten Commandments were written. This was to be very ornate with <u>small</u> decorations, inside and out, and topped with two large statues of angels, called cherubim.

The Ark was to be <u>brought</u> inside a tent made of leather and woven wool and fine linen, held up by four tent poles. This tent was called the Tabernacle, and was embroidered royally. Inside was an <u>altar</u> and a seven-branched candlestick. There was a curtain hanging to hide the Ark. The space inside this curtain was called the Holy of Holies.

Just outside was another <u>altar</u>, this one for <u>offering</u> sacrifices. There was also a great curtained court around the Tabernacle. <u>All</u> inside was holy ground. It was the meeting place of God and men.

L E S S O N

12

/u/ sound in book

wooded
goodbye
plural
looking
merciful
crooked
woman
pulled
cookbook
pushed
stood
toward
bookshelf
understood
woolen

BONUS

during

NAME ______________________

The **/u/** sound in b**oo**k is spelled **oo** (f**oo**t), **o** (t**o**ward), or **u** (p**u**t).

A Sort by Syllable

Each box below has a different spelling of the /**u**/ sound in b**oo**k. On each line, write a list word that has the same spelling of this sound as the one in the box.

o	______________________
	______________________
oo	______________________
	______________________
	______________________
	______________________
	______________________
	______________________
	______________________
	______________________
	______________________
u	______________________
	______________________
	______________________
	______________________
	______________________

NAME ______________________________

B Definitions

Below are given definitions to the words found in the list. Write the appropriate word in the space provided next to the definition.

throughout the course of	1. ____________
form of a word to show more than one	2. ____________
dragged	3. ____________
pressed against with force	4. ____________
covered with trees	5. ____________
lady	6. ____________
a shelf for holding books	7. ____________
was standing	8. ____________
made of wool	9. ____________
in the direction of	10. ____________
having or showing mercy or compassion	11. ____________
seeing	12. ____________
a farewell remark; farewell	13. ____________
a book of cooking recipes and directions	14. ____________
having bends and curves	15. ____________
accepted as settled	16. ____________

NAME ______________________

In each sentence below, there is a blank corresponding to one of the words found in the word list. Write the missing word in the space next to the sentence.

Dad built a ___ for our religion books.	1. ____________
We found the path in the park was not straight but ___.	2. ____________
My sister sang in the choir ___ the Mass.	3. ____________
Irene waved ___ to her grandfather as he was leaving.	4. ____________
My mother wrote a ___ of her favorite Lenten recipes.	5. ____________
The baby was ___ at his mother.	6. ____________
We must be ___ if we wish mercy for ourselves.	7. ____________
The ___ form of knife is knives.	8. ____________
Susan ___ her sweater out of the drawer.	9. ____________
The toddler laughed as she ___ the door shut.	10. ____________
I ___ next to first base for the baseball game.	11. ____________
The toddler rushed ___ his mother when she returned.	12. ____________
Once Dad pointed out my math errors, I ___ what I had done wrong.	13. ____________
The deer and rabbits were running in the large ___ area.	14. ____________
God created Eve, the first ___, from Adam's rib.	15. ____________
We gave Dad a ___ scarf for Christmas.	16. ____________

NAME ____________________

D Story Time

Read the following story, paying attention to the underlined words. Notice how they use the spelling rule to the right.

The **u** sound in b**oo**k is spelled **oo** (f**oo**t), **o** (t**o**ward), or **u** (p**u**t).

Into the Holy Land

After Moses' death, Joshua became the leader of God's people. The Israelites prepared to enter the Holy Land. By Joshua's order, they began to march. The priests in front of the soldiers took the Ark of the Covenant. Soon they came to the banks of the Jordan River. They could not take time to look at the danger; they had to cross it, even though it was flooded. When the priests carrying the Ark stepped into the river, it stopped flowing and a dry passage was in front of the people so they could enter their land safely. The priests stood still in the river bed holding the sacred Ark, until the whole nation of Israel, men, women, and children, passed through.

The people of God put up their tents on the other side of the river, midway between the Jordan and the city of Jericho. They were to take this city and all the other cities in the land of Canaan, and overcome the pagan peoples throughout the land. This was going to be God's country, and those in it were to be His faithful subjects.

The Ark is carried around Jericho.

Joshua commands the sun to stand still.

NAME ______________________________

LESSON 13

/oo/ sound in boot

tools
loose
produce
choose
students
grew
include
whose
renew
shoes
flute
prove
true
movement
lose

BONUS

canoe

The /**oo**/ sound in b**oo**t is spelled **oo** (t**oo**), **o** (t**o**), **oe** (sh**oe**) **ew** (gr**ew**), **ue** (d**ue**), or **u** (incl**u**de).

A Sort by Syllable

Each box below has a different spelling of the /**oo**/ sound in b**oo**t. On each line, write a list word that has the same spelling of this sound as the one in the box.

ew	______________________ ______________________
o	______________________ ______________________ ______________________ ______________________
oe	______________________ ______________________
oo	______________________ ______________________ ______________________
u	______________________ ______________________ ______________________ ______________________
ue	______________________

NAME ______________________________

B Definitions

Below are given definitions to the words found in the list. Write the appropriate word in the space provided next to the definition.

the act of moving	1. ________
pupils; people who study	2. ________
to put together; to make	3. ________
of whom	4. ________
instruments for work, such as saws and hammers	5. ________
outer coverings for feet	6. ________
to take in or have as a part	7. ________
musical instrument	8. ________
long light narrow boat	9. ________
to select	10. ________
not tight	11. ________
to mislay; not to find	12. ________
increased in size	13. ________
corresponding to reality; real	14. ________
to demonstrate	15. ________
to make or become new, fresh, or strong again	16. ________

NAME ____________________

In each sentence below, there is a blank corresponding to one of the words found in the word list. Write the missing word in the space next to the sentence.

The active ___ of the baby showed that she was no longer sick.	1. ________
The ___ were tested on their knowledge of religion.	2. ________
My uncle wants to ___ more Catholic songbooks for our church.	3. ________
Jesus said to the Apostles: "___ sins you shall forgive, they are forgiven."	4. ________
My father keeps his ___ in the toolbox in the basement.	5. ________
My dad sells sandals, boots, slippers, and ___.	6. ________
My mother told me to ___ my little brother in my games.	7. ________
Mom wants us to ___ our library cards for another year.	8. ________
Father Lewis rowed the ___ on the Shenandoah River.	9. ________
Little Teresa found it hard to ___ among the gifts.	10. ________
My sister had a ___ tooth for a week.	11. ________
My brother was afraid he would ___ his money at the gym.	12. ________
Grandfather thinks I ___ two inches this past year.	13. ________
Danny ran the race to ___ that he could run fast.	14. ________
The Catholic Church is the one ___ Church founded by Jesus.	15. ________
Lucy plays the ___ in the children's orchestra.	16. ________

NAME ______________________________

D Story Time

Read the following story, paying attention to the underlined words. Notice how they use the spelling rule to the right.

The /**oo**/ sound in b**oo**t is spelled **oo**, **o**, **oe**, **ew**, **ue**, or **u**.

The Five Kings

The Israelites were feared by the pagans in the land because they had heard of the God Who protected His people against their enemies. After the Jews had conquered Jericho, they continued taking the Promised Land for themselves as God directed. Some of the pagan kings were frightened. Some believed it was proof that the Israelites worshiped the true God. Others decided to work together to overcome Joshua and his men.

So it came about that the Children of Israel were fighting the armies of five kings. It was a vicious battle. Joshua had surprised the enemy during the night. The fight lasted into the day. If the sun set, the kings would be able to rest and regroup their armies. This could make things harder for the Jews. Full of confidence that they would not lose the battle, Joshua prayed to God that the day would not end before they were victorious. So God made the sun stand still in the sky, and its light shone until the enemy was defeated.

NAME ______________________________

LESSON

14

/ou/ sound in out

power

flowers

shouted

ground

vowel

hours

thousands

house

amount

count

pounds

round

brown

mouth

south

BONUS

allowed

The /**ou**/ sound in **ou**t is usually spelled **ou** or **ow.**

A Sort by Syllable

Each box below has a different spelling of the /**ou**/ sound in **ou**t. On each line, write a list word that has the same spelling of this sound as the one in the box.

ou	______________________ ______________________ ______________________ ______________________ ______________________ ______________________ ______________________ ______________________ ______________________ ______________________ ______________________
ow	______________________ ______________________ ______________________ ______________________ ______________________

NAME ______________________________

B Definitions

Below are given definitions to the words found in the list. Write the appropriate word in the space provided next to the definition.

Definition	
given permission for	1. ____________
the total number	2. ____________
forming a circle	3. ____________
soil; earth; dry land	4. ____________
a building in which people live	5. ____________
strength	6. ____________
made a sudden loud cry	7. ____________
tens of hundreds	8. ____________
a color like that of chocolate	9. ____________
add up	10. ____________
a letter representing a sound; a, e, i, o, u	11. ____________
measures of weight, 16 ounces each	12. ____________
an opening for eating	13. ____________
the opposite of north	14. ____________
the twenty-four divisions of a day	15. ____________
plants grown for their blossoms; the blossoms of such a plant	16. ____________

NAME ____________________

In each sentence below, there is a blank corresponding to one of the words found in the word list. Write the missing word in the space next to the sentence.

Father Powell has never ___ running in the church.	1. ________
We picked pink and red ___ for the May Crowning.	2. ________
Sister McDow found a kitten lying on the ___.	3. ________
Our family is renting a ___ near our church.	4. ________
The ___ of God created the whole world.	5. ________
"The fish are biting!" Grandpa ___.	6. ________
The little, white, ___ Host is the Body and Blood of Jesus.	7. ________
The Franciscan nuns wore a ___ habit.	8. ________
That large statue of the Sacred Heart must weigh a hundred ___.	9. ________
It is warmer in the ___ than in the north.	10. ________
The ushers at church had to ___ the collection from Mass.	11. ________
There were ___ of ants in my front yard!	12. ________
We receive a great ___ of grace when we go to Holy Communion.	13. ________
A ___, such as *a*, *e*, *i*, *o*, or *u*, gives a word its sound.	14. ________
My ___ was sore after visiting the dentist.	15. ________
Jesus spent three ___ dying on the cross.	16. ________

NAME ______________________________

D Story Time

Read the following story, paying attention to the underlined words. Notice how they use the spelling rule to the right.

The /**ou**/ sound in **ou**t is usually spelled **ou** or **ow.**

Samson's Long Hair

Samson was a popular hero among the Israelites. The Bible shows him as a man dedicated to God from the cradle. His long hair marked him as a man of God in a special way. It was like the backward collar and black clothes of a priest, a badge of office. But this adornment was not what made him strong and powerful.

When Samson's hair was cut off, it was a sign to the world that he abandoned his first dedication to God. When that happened, God took away his strength. During his captivity, Samson made a good act of contrition and God, the Source of his strength, gave back to him all his power.

Samson's captors led him into a giant temple in order to expose the once great captain to their mockery. The blind and apparently feeble Samson asked the slave who was leading him to allow him to rest against the pillars of the temple. This temple was almost like a coliseum, or stadium. Within it were many of the greatest warriors and leaders of the Philistines who had gathered to celebrate their victory with shouts of conquest. Samson prayed for God to give him strength and then, with all his might, wedged himself between two mighty pillars and forced them apart. The weight of the thousands of assembled Philistines proved too much for the structure, now weakened without its pillars. The roof and balconies collapsed and crushed the assembled crowds.

SAMSON PUSHES APART THE PILLARS WITH THE GRACE OF GOD.

Samuel is presented to Eli in the Temple.

LESSON

15

/ng/ sound in sing

fingers
belong
feeling
wrongdoing
evening
language
youngest
hunting
English
among
morning
nothing
drink
wings
building

BONUS

along

NAME ____________________

The **/ng/** sound in si**ng** is spelled **ng**.
Before a **k**, it is spelled **n**, as in si**n**k.

A Sort by Syllable

Each box below has a different spelling of the **/ng/** sound in si**ng**. On each line, write a list word that has the same spelling of this sound as the one in the box.

n	____________________
ng	____________________ ____________________ ____________________ ____________________ ____________________ ____________________ ____________________ ____________________ ____________________ ____________________ ____________________ ____________________ ____________________ ____________________ ____________________

NAME ______________________

B Definitions

Below are given definitions to the words found in the list. Write the appropriate word in the space provided next to the definition.

searching for wild animals in order to capture or kill	1. ______
the later and final part of the day	2. ______
onward; together	3. ______
any liquid swallowed to quench thirst; beverage	4. ______
words used by people of the same nation	5. ______
not anything	6. ______
in the middle of	7. ______
the most young	8. ______
body parts with which a bird or insect flies	9. ______
doing what is not right	10. ______
a permanent structure for dwelling or working	11. ______
to be the property of	12. ______
body parts located at the end of the hand	13. ______
sensing with one's skin	14. ______
the early part of the day	15. ______
the language of the United States; the inhabitants of England	16. ______

NAME ______________________________

C Missing Words

In each sentence below, there is a blank corresponding to one of the words found in the word list. Write the missing word in the space next to the sentence.

Jesus called Matthew to come ___ with Him as an apostle.	1. ______________
Young John was ___ the apostles chosen by Jesus.	2. ______________
The chalices ___ to Father Lang.	3. ______________
The monks asked the bishop if they could build a new ___.	4. ______________
Jesus taught us that we must give ___ to the thirsty.	5. ______________
___ Catholics were killed in England just for being Catholic.	6. ______________
Our family spent the ___ together, talking, singing, and sharing our lives with each other.	7. ______________
I was ___ cold, so Mom brought me a sweater.	8. ______________
The piano players' ___ moved so fast one could hardly see them.	9. ______________
Dad took my brothers ___ and fishing last week.	10. ______________
My uncle said we should learn Spanish as well as the English ___.	11. ______________
My grandfather sleeps late in the ___.	12. ______________
When Herod asked Jesus questions, He remained silent and said ___.	13. ______________
The ___ on the butterfly were a bright yellow.	14. ______________
Many are convicted of ___ even though they are innocent.	15. ______________
St. John was very young; in fact, he was the ___ apostle.	16. ______________

NAME ______________________________

D Story Time

Read the following story, paying attention to the underlined words. Notice how they use the spelling rule to the right.

> The **/ng/** sound in si**ng** is spelled **ng**. Before a **k**, it is spelled **n**, as in si**n**k.

A Holy Prophet of God

In the mountain country near the center of Palestine lived a holy, God-fearing man and his wife, Anna. She was sad, because she had no children. Yet neither this nor anything else swayed her from her devotion to God. Every year, she and her husband thanked Him, offering sacrifice and worship to Him before the holy Ark, and every year she asked God for a son. She promised to give her son back to the Lord, and that he would serve Him for his whole life. Her faith in God did not falter, though He did not answer her prayers immediately.

So it came to pass that finally Anna gave birth to a baby boy. She named him Samuel. One morning, when he was five years old, she decided to bring her son to Silo, where the Ark was kept, to give him to God. She and her husband brought gifts for the priest and calves to sacrifice to God. They stayed and worshiped in that holy building, the temple, and then went back home, leaving Samuel in God's house, where he now belonged.

Thus it was that Samuel was raised in the temple among the priests, and he grew to be very close to God. The people recognized his holiness. When Samuel became judge over all Israel, he was able to lead the people back to God.

NAME ______________________________

LESSON 16

/or/ sound in oar

order
floor
score
northern
yourself
course
horse
majority
tore
corner
north
report
force
board
correctly

BONUS

forward

The /**or**/ sound in **oar** is spelled **oar (soar)**, **or (organ)**, **ore (tore)**, **our** (f**our**), or **oor** (d**oor**).

A Sort by Syllable

Each box below has a different spelling of the /**or**/ sound in **oar**. On each line, write a list word that has the same spelling of this sound as the one in the box.

oar	______________
oor	______________
or	______________
	______________
	______________
	______________
	______________
	______________
	______________
	______________
	______________
	______________
ore	______________
	______________
our	______________
	______________

NAME ____________________

B Definitions

Below are given definitions to the words found in the list. Write the appropriate word in the space provided next to the definition.

the place where two streets meet	1. ________
class or subject for study	2. ________
compel	3. ________
pulled something apart or ripped it into two pieces	4. ________
to or toward what is ahead	5. ________
a large, hoofed animal	6. ________
sawed piece of lumber	7. ________
a number greater than half of a total	8. ________
the direction opposite to the south	9. ________
of or related to the north	10. ________
command	11. ________
to describe or tell something; a formal account	12. ________
accurately	13. ________
part of a room on which one stands	14. ________
your own self	15. ________
a record of points made or lost	16. ________

NAME ______________________

In each sentence below, there is a blank corresponding to one of the words found in the word list. Write the missing word in the space next to the sentence.

The famous painting showed St. Joseph, a carpenter, sawing a ___.	1. ______
The shrine is located at the ___ of Main and South Streets.	2. ______
James copied the paragraph neatly and ___.	3. ______
My brother enrolled in the Bible ___ at the parish.	4. ______
Several of the men in the parish worked on waxing the church ___.	5. ______
Herod tried to ___ Jesus to answer him, but He would not.	6. ______
We anxiously looked ___ to attending my brother's first baseball game.	7. ______
Sally ___ the picture in half.	8. ______
St. Joan rode her ___ into the battle.	9. ______
The ___ of citizens voted for the pro-life candidate.	10. ______
My uncle, who likes cooler weather, traveled ___ for his vacation.	11. ______
Our relatives live in the ___ part of Ireland.	12. ______
The general gave an ___ to the soldiers to move out.	13. ______
The scout, upon returning, gave a detailed ___ on the enemy stronghold.	14. ______
My dad said he bowled a great game and had an awesome ___.	15. ______
No, you don't need any help! Wash the dishes ___!	16. ______

NAME ____________________

D Story Time

Read the following story, paying attention to the underlined words. Notice how they use the spelling rule to the right.

The /**or**/ sound in **oar** is spelled **oar**, **or**, **ore**, **our**, or **oor**.

Anointing of Saul

Samuel grew to be an old man. He had changed Israel from a wicked nation to a nation where God was loved and obeyed by many. God guided him so that he led Israel wisely and well. The land was peaceful and the people fared well. But they were not content with living according to the rule of God through His judges. They wanted to have a king like the other nations around them. They tried to order Samuel to find them a king.

Such a course of action disgusted Samuel. Israel didn't need a king. God was their King and He would take care of them. Since the people insisted, Samuel decided not to argue anymore and instead asked God.

God said that they could have a king, but it would not make them happy. A king would do much harm. He would force their sons to serve in his army. He would take their property and give it to his friends. He would make them pay high taxes. Then they would beg God to be rid of him, but God would not listen to them.

Still, because the people had asked and God had ordered it, Samuel anointed Saul the first king of Israel.

Samuel meets Saul.

JOSEPH FORGIVES HIS BROTHERS FOR THEIR CRIME.

NAME ______________________________

LESSON

17

/ur/ sound in urn

surface
wonder
certain
workers
direct
teacher
general
heard
brother
world
members
current
observe
return
church

BONUS

surprise

The /**ur**/ sound in **ur**n is spelled **ur** (f**ur**), **er** (h**er**), **ir** (g**ir**l), **or** (w**or**ld), or **ear** (**ear**n).

A Sort by Syllable

Each box below has a different spelling of the /**ur**/ sound in **ur**n. On each line, write a list word that has the same spelling of this sound as the one in the box.

ear	______________________________
er	______________________________
	______________________________
	______________________________
	______________________________
	______________________________
	______________________________
	______________________________
ir	______________________________
or	______________________________
	______________________________
ur	______________________________
	______________________________
	______________________________
	______________________________
	______________________________

NAME ______________________________

B Definitions

Below are given definitions to the words found in the list. Write the appropriate word in the space provided next to the definition.

to watch	1. ________
the earth	2. ________
a person of high rank in the military	3. ________
people who labor	4. ________
to be curious	5. ________
a building for worship	6. ________
come back	7. ________
to show or tell the way	8. ________
sure; being fixed or settled	9. ________
occurring at the present time	10. ________
listened to	11. ________
the outside of an object; exterior; cover	12. ________
astonishment	13. ________
one who instructs	14. ________
individuals making up a group	15. ________
a boy or a man who has a parent in common with another	16. ________

J.M.J.

Jesus, Mary, Joseph, I love You. Save souls!

NAME ____________________

In each sentence below, there is a blank corresponding to one of the words found in the word list. Write the missing word in the space next to the sentence.

All over the ___, people are hungry for truth as well as food.	1. ____________
Rosemary likes to clean the white ___ of the kitchen counter.	2. ____________
Jesus taught that we should treat everyone as a ___ in Christ.	3. ____________
The ___ news is that Father Churchill will remain pastor of our parish.	4. ____________
Her mother will ___ us to the apple orchard.	5. ____________
Sometimes my brothers ___ what they will be when they grow up!	6. ____________
The children ___ a loud noise outside the house.	7. ____________
Every day we can ___ the growth of our little plant.	8. ____________
The ___ of the Knights of Columbus were asked to help the poor.	9. ____________
We can be ___ that Jesus loves us more than we can imagine.	10. ____________
The ___ at the factory were happy they had a full-time job.	11. ____________
The ___ of the army always started the day with a prayer for his men.	12. ____________
Sharon wears her prettiest dresses to ___ on Sunday.	13. ____________
The father wept when he saw his son ___ after being gone so long.	14. ____________
Since Jesus often taught in the Temple, he was addressed as a ___.	15. ____________
The birthday party was a ___ for my aunt.	16. ____________

NAME ____________________

D Story Time

Read the following story, paying attention to the underlined words. Notice how they use the spelling rule to the right.

The **/ur/** sound in **ur**n is spelled **ur**, **er**, **ir**, **or**, or **ear**.

Types of Christ

There are many persons in the Old Testament who remind us of Our Lord Jesus Christ. They endured many sufferings as Christ did in His life. They are called types of Christ. Moses, Isaac, and Melchisedek are just a few whose lives reflect the life of Our Lord.

One of the most well-known types of Christ is Joseph. He went into Egypt ahead of his brothers and eventually brought them there to save their lives. Our Lord went on ahead of us, to bring us safely to Heaven and save our souls. Christ, like Joseph, was sold for a few pieces of silver. Joseph was innocent and suffered for crimes he did not commit. So did Christ, the Holy One of God, suffer for our sins. Joseph forgave his brothers for their crime. We can be certain that Jesus will forgive us of our sins if we are sorry for them. Jesus was born so that anyone in the world could be saved if he or she would love God, obey His Commandments, and be sorry for sins. The Catholic Church, founded by Jesus, is our means of salvation.

NAME

Lesson Review

Lesson 10	Lesson 11	Lesson 12	Lesson 13
folded	outlaw	wooded	tools
control	all right	goodbye	loose
stone	cause	plural	produce
known	naughty	looking	choose
soldiers	oftentimes	merciful	students
police	brought	crooked	grew
shoulder	caught	woman	include
bones	autumn	pulled	whose
rolled	bought	cookbook	renew
slowly	cross	pushed	shoes
clothes	drawing	stood	flute
although	office	toward	prove
suppose	across	bookshelf	true
hello	chalk	understood	movement
coast	small	woolen	lose
BONUS	BONUS	BONUS	BONUS
shown	already	during	canoe

NAME ______________________________

Tips from your *Guardian Angel*

- Pronounce each word for correct spelling.
- Say the word, spell it, and say it again.
- Divide each word into syllables.
- Take an oral pretest of all these words, then write each misspelled word three times.

Lesson 14	Lesson 15	Lesson 16	Lesson 17
power	fingers	order	surface
flowers	belong	floor	wonder
shouted	feeling	score	certain
ground	wrongdoing	northern	workers
vowel	evening	yourself	direct
hours	language	course	teacher
thousands	youngest	horse	general
house	hunting	majority	heard
amount	English	forest	brother
count	among	corner	world
pounds	morning	north	members
round	nothing	report	current
brown	drink	force	observe
mouth	wings	board	return
south	building	correctly	church
BONUS	**BONUS**	**BONUS**	**BONUS**
allowed	along	forward	surprise

J.M.J.

Jesus, Mary, Joseph, I love You. Save souls!

LESSON

19

-ed sounds

stretched
happened
printed
filled
entered
joined
agreed
located
received
lifted
resulted
measured
covered
smiled
picked

BONUS

reached

NAME ____________________

Past-tense words ending in **-ed** make the /**ed**/ sound when the root ends with **d** or **t**; otherwise, the ending **-ed** makes the **/d/** or /**t**/ sound.

A Sort by Syllable

Each box below has a different spelling of the **-ed** sound. On each line, write a list word that has the same spelling of this sound as the one in the box.

d	____________________ ____________________ ____________________ ____________________ ____________________ ____________________ ____________________ ____________________ ____________________
t	____________________ ____________________ ____________________
ed	____________________ ____________________ ____________________ ____________________

NAME ______________________

B Definitions

Below are given definitions to the words found in the list. Write the appropriate word in the space provided next to the definition.

took place	1. ______
went into	2. ______
raised from a lower to a higher position	3. ______
spread something over or on	4. ______
copied	5. ______
took something given	6. ______
found out the size of	7. ______
placed; found	8. ______
occupied fully	9. ______
grinned	10. ______
chose	11. ______
had the same opinion	12. ______
extended one's arms in order to grasp something	13. ______
spread out	14. ______
came about as an effect or consequence	15. ______
became a member of	16. ______

NAME ______________________________

In each sentence below, there is a blank corresponding to one of the words found in the word list. Write the missing word in the space next to the sentence.

Ken got out of bed and ___ his arms before saying his morning prayers.	1. ____________
The angel Gabriel told Mary that she was ___ with grace.	2. ____________
Father James made the Sign of the Cross as he ___ the church.	3. ____________
Mark ___ the boys' basketball team last week.	4. ____________
Beth ___ her award for outstanding achievement in gymnastics.	5. ____________
Saint Joseph ___ the length of the board.	6. ____________
The judges ___ the contest winner.	7. ____________
Dad and Mom ___ that I should go.	8. ____________
Our friendly baby ___ at everyone in church.	9. ____________
The priest carefully ___ the chalice with the blessed cloth.	10. ____________
Her lack of study ___ in poor grades.	11. ____________
The accident ___ yesterday.	12. ____________
Johnny ___ the heavy groceries out of the car.	13. ____________
Little Mary ___ high for the grapes.	14. ____________
Our house is ___ one block from church.	15. ____________
Jane carefully ___ all the words from her spelling page.	16. ____________

NAME ____________________

D Story Time

Read the following story, paying attention to the underlined words. Notice how they use the spelling rule to the right.

Past-tense words ending in **-ed** make the /**d**/, /**t**/, or /**ed**/ sound.

Saul the King

Samuel taught King Saul how to walk in God's ways, and, for a while, the young king was righteous in the eyes of God and man. One time, a nation of savage robbers across the Jordan waged war on Israel. Saul led the Hebrews into battle, and since he trusted in God and kept His Laws, the enemy was overcome and Saul was victorious. Israel celebrated with a huge feast and songs, and Saul was a hero.

Years went by and Saul began to change. He grew proud. He no longer obeyed God. The Philistines were making war against him. His soldiers were deserting. Samuel, now an aged man, went to Saul and told him that God would no longer bless him, and that no man of Saul's family would reign as king. Then Samuel, too, left him. This all happened because Saul put his own will before God.

Saul dies in battle.

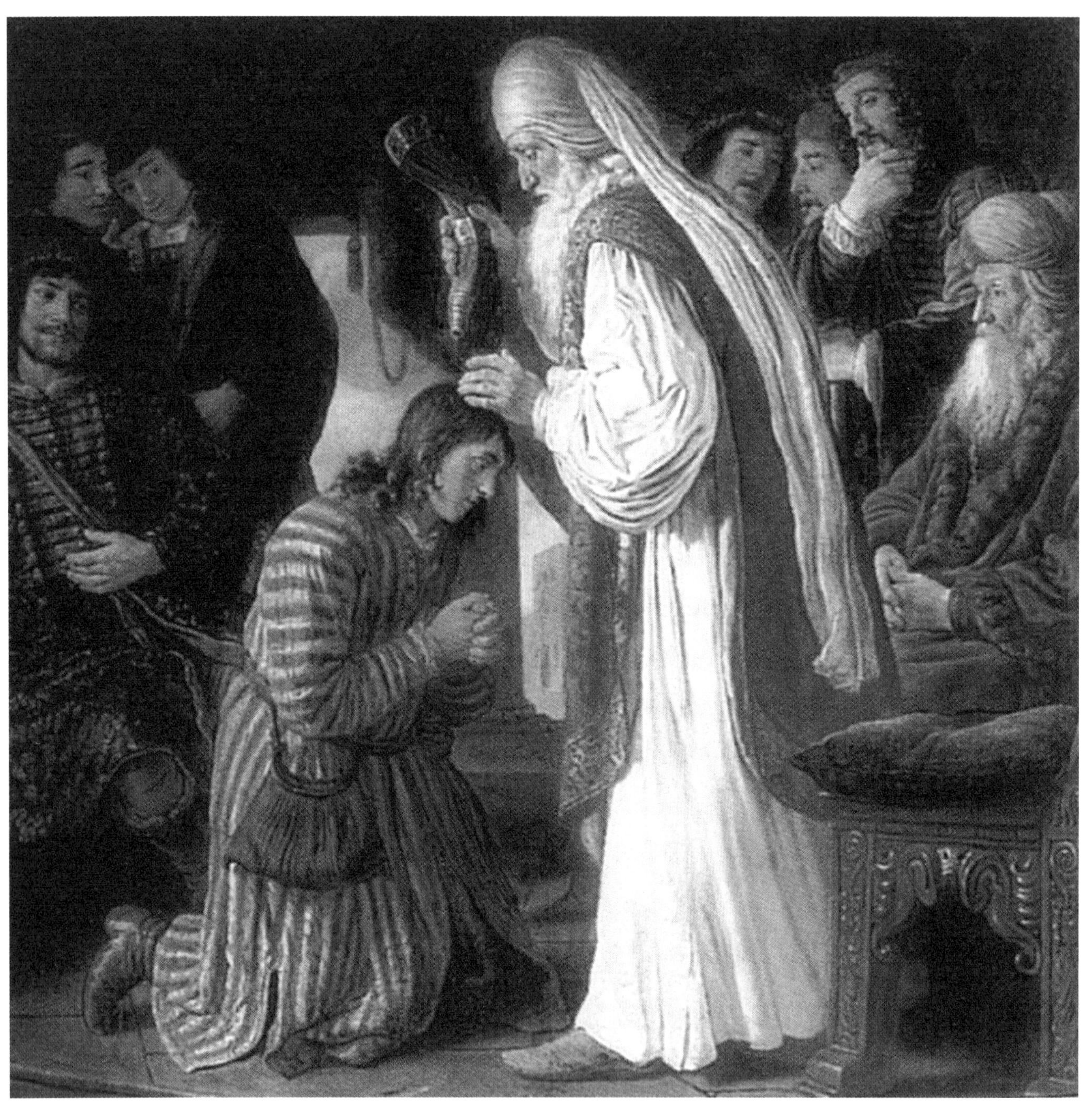

Samuel anoints David.

NAME ______________________________

LESSON 20

Unaccented syllables

lemon
burden
sudden
kingdom
towel
lawful
medium
mortal
willful
missal
sinful
normal
fashion
passion
parrot

BONUS

awake

The sound of the vowel in an unaccented syllable often is an /**uh**/ sound.

A Sort by Syllable

Each box below has a different spelling of the /**uh**/ sound. On each line, write a list word that has the same spelling of this sound as the one in the box.

a	____________ ____________ ____________ ____________
e	____________ ____________ ____________
io	____________ ____________
o	____________ ____________ ____________
u	____________ ____________ ____________ ____________

NAME ______________________________

B Definitions

Below are given definitions to the words found in the list. Write the appropriate word in the space provided next to the definition.

of the regular or usual kind	1. ______________
capable of causing death	2. ______________
book containing Mass prayers	3. ______________
a load carried with difficulty	4. ______________
quick or unexpected	5. ______________
a cloth for wiping or drying	6. ______________
the suffering and death of Christ	7. ______________
in the middle in amount or degree or quality	8. ______________
a style, as of dressing or behaving	9. ______________
a country whose ruler is a king or queen	10. ______________
an oval yellow fruit with a sour juice	11. ______________
a brightly colored tropical bird with a strong hooked bill	12. ______________
not sleeping	13. ______________
permitted by law	14. ______________
wicked; being full of sin	15. ______________
stubbornly determined to have one's own way; done deliberately	16. ______________

NAME ______________________________

In each sentence below, there is a blank corresponding to one of the words found in the word list. Write the missing word in the space next to the sentence.

He said that carrying his brother was not a ___.	1. ________
The loud barking kept the neighborhood ___.	2. ________
King Solomon's ___ had many riches.	3. ________
Our Lord dried the feet of His apostles with a ___.	4. ________
Dad likes his meat cooked ___ rare and not well done.	5. ________
St. Mary Magdalen rejected her ___ life.	6. ________
The nurse said his blood pressure was ___.	7. ________
A ___ jolt of lightning took us by surprise.	8. ________
The ___ of Christ is our salvation.	9. ________
Joey was being stubborn and ___ when he would not follow his father's good advice.	10. ________
In the United States, it is not ___ to drive on the left side of the road.	11. ________
Ricky liked the bright yellow ___ at the zoo.	12. ________
Monica ate the cake with the ___ frosting.	13. ________
The latest ___ in men's ties is bright colors.	14. ________
A ___ sin is a serious offense against God.	15. ________
She left her ___ in the pew at St. Ann's Church.	16. ________

NAME ______________________

D Story Time

Read the following story, paying attention to the underlined words. Notice how they use the spelling rule to the right.

The sound of the vowel in an unaccented syllable often is an /**uh**/ sound.

The Anointing of David

One day, the people of Bethlehem saw a man climbing slowly up the winding road to the hilltop, driving a calf before him. It was Samuel, the old prophet, and he was carrying a bottle of olive oil in his hand. Once there, he offered the calf in sacrifice to God, with all the people of the town present. Then he went to the house of Jesse. There he asked to see each of Jesse's sons, one by one. When each was brought before him, the old man would ask God, "Is this the Lord's anointed?" Each time the Lord replied that he was not, so the next son would enter.

Then David, the youngest son, was brought before Samuel. He had been in the hills, sitting on a rock and singing to his sheep. When David entered the house, Samuel was waiting. He saw the handsome boy, tall and strong for his age. God whispered to the prophet, "Stand up and anoint him; this is the one."

So Samuel stood in front of the boy and poured the oil on his head. Then Samuel said that he wanted David to come study with him. From then on, David spent some of his time with Samuel, and some of it at home. One day, Samuel took David aside and told him why he had been anointed: God had chosen him to be the king over the kingdom of Israel after Saul's death. Samuel took great pains to teach David, his pupil, how to rule others in a lawful way, with justice and kindness.

LESSON

21

Unaccented syllables

final
human
legal
metal
poem
mental
total
medal
equal
ankle
local
marvel
moral
major
factor

BONUS

ability

NAME ______________________________

The sound of the vowel in an unaccented syllable often is an /**uh**/ sound.

A Sort by Syllable

Each box below has a different spelling of the /**uh**/ sound. On each line, write a list word that has the same spelling of this sound as the one in the box.

a	______________
al	______________
	______________
	______________
	______________
	______________
	______________
	______________
	______________
	______________
an	______________
el	______________
em	______________
le	______________
or	______________
	______________

NAME ______________________________

B Definitions

Below are given definitions to the words found in the list. Write the appropriate word in the space provided next to the definition.

power to do something	1. ________
a piece of metal with design and words in honor of a special person or event	2. ________
relating to the mind	3. ________
nearby	4. ________
exactly the same in number or quality	5. ________
a writing often having rhyme or rhythm which tells a story or describes a feeling	6. ________
permitted by law; having to do with law	7. ________
an entire amount	8. ________
occurring at the end	9. ________
something that helps in getting a result; to determine	10. ________
a substance which has a shiny appearance and is a good conductor of electricity	11. ________
to wonder; be amazed	12. ________
the lesson about right or wrong	13. ________
the joint between the foot and leg	14. ________
a person with a body and a soul	15. ________
greater in number or quality; significant	16. ________

NAME ____________________

C Missing Words

In each sentence below, there is a blank corresponding to one of the words found in the word list. Write the missing word in the space next to the sentence.

My dad, a lawyer, provides ___ information to help people.	1. ________
Jane wrote a ___ to St. Joseph.	2. ________
Dad had a great ___ for playing basketball.	3. ________
Tommy hurt his ___ while racing at the parish picnic.	4. ________
The St. Benedict ___ is a powerful sacramental.	5. ________
My sister is a nurse at the clinic and helps people with ___ disabilities.	6. ________
Gabriel made a ___ improvement in his grades.	7. ________
We went to Mass at the ___ parish church.	8. ________
Jesus is both ___ and divine.	9. ________
We should ___ at the power of God when we look at the world around us.	10. ________
The boys had an ___ number of dimes.	11. ________
The children talked about the ___ of the story.	12. ________
The statue in church was made of ___.	13. ________
The ___ cost of the books was $25.	14. ________
The weather will not be a ___, since the event will be inside.	15. ________
Jesus' ___ words were, "It is finished."	16. ________

NAME ______________________________

D Story Time

Read the following story, paying attention to the underlined words. Notice how they use the spelling rule to the right.

> The sound of the vowel in an unaccented syllable often is an /**uh**/ sound.

David, God's King

It was David, a young boy, who was the one person in the nation of Israel brave enough to fight the giant Goliath. This deed, a battle between a boy and a giant, brought David to the attention of King Saul. But Saul was growing angry and bitter, and he grew to hate David, who had to go into hiding to save his own life. Even though Saul was trying to kill him, David realized that Saul, too, was once anointed by God. David would not allow anyone to harm the king.

When Saul died, there was no king in Israel. David knew he was to be king, but he was not sure what to do next. After a prayerful and painful time, he asked the priests to tell him what God wanted.

Some of Saul's followers gathered an army to fight against him, but David's army always crushed his enemies. The people knew how shameful it was to fight against their youthful hero. Finally, all the tribes chose David to be their king. So David then ruled over all of the nation of Israel. He was only thirty years old.

David slays Goliath.

DAVID PLAYS THE HARP AND SINGS THE PRAISES OF THE LORD.

LESSON

22

One vowel sound

third
march
your
point
serve
voice
large
there
start
terms
sharp
chart
birds
where
solve

BONUS

first

NAME ____________________

Words having only one vowel sound and syllable may never be divided in writing or spelling.

A Sort by Syllable

Sort the words by the sound of the vowel. Remember that a vowel sound can have more than one spelling. Write all the words with that sound. The spellings of the sound may differ.

f**ar**	____________________ ____________________ ____________________ ____________________ ____________________
all	____________________
air	____________________ ____________________
t**oy**	____________________ ____________________
f**ur**	____________________ ____________________ ____________________ ____________________ ____________________
p**ure**	____________________

NAME ______________________________

B Definitions

Below are given definitions to the words found in the list. Write the appropriate word in the space provided next to the definition.

animals with wings and feathers	1. ____________
a sharp or tapered end, such as of a pencil	2. ____________
a sheet giving information in a table form	3. ____________
belonging to you	4. ____________
before any other	5. ____________
to find the answer	6. ____________
in what place	7. ____________
big	8. ____________
walk briskly and rhythmically	9. ____________
in that place	10. ____________
to give service; to be of use	11. ____________
having a thin edge like a knife; pointed	12. ____________
begin	13. ____________
words or expressions; details	14. ____________
comes after second	15. ____________
sound produced through the mouth in speaking or singing	16. ____________

J.M.J.

Jesus, Mary, Joseph, I love You. Save souls!

NAME ____________________

C Missing Words

In each sentence below, there is a blank corresponding to one of the words found in the word list. Write the missing word in the space next to the sentence.

Alex had good reasons for not being ___.	1. ________
The Scarlet Macaw and King Penguin are types of rare ___.	2. ________
___ is the matching shoe?	3. ________
Paul could not ___ with the band last night.	4. ________
The arrow had a very ___ point.	5. ________
My ___ Communion was the happiest day of my life.	6. ________
The ___ Commandment tells us to keep the Sabbath holy.	7. ________
The singer was famous for her beautiful ___.	8. ________
Mary sharpened the pencil to a very sharp ___.	9. ________
Dominic could not ___ the division problem.	10. ________
Christ came to ___ and not to be served.	11. ________
___ the day with a healthy breakfast.	12. ________
Where are ___ religion books?	13. ________
Daniel made a ___ of all his religion grades for the past six months.	14. ________
Mom said I should find words or ___ to substitute for my vocabulary list.	15. ________
I like being the oldest in a ___ family.	16. ________

NAME ____________________

D Story Time

Read the following story, paying attention to the underlined words. Notice how they use the spelling rule to the right.

Words having only one vowel sound and syllable may never be divided.

The Psalms

David was not only a king and a warrior, but also a gifted poet and musician. His life was filled with loyalty to God and zeal for God's glory. His own devotion set an example for his people to follow, and they grew in their love for God. It was he who wrote the Psalms that praise God our Creator.

David's Psalms give words to every joy and sorrow in the heart of man. They are full of the sun and the wind, the rain and the stars, the deep blue sky and the break of day. In them, the trees of the forest clap their hands before God, and the Lord, like a shepherd, cares tenderly for His people. Men, like the antelopes in the desert, long for God as the thirsty beast longs for springs of clear water. God has allowed men to be in charge of His creation, the birds of the air, and the fishes of the sea.

David was a man with a holy soul and a great heart, and his prayers reflect this. They are the confident prayers of the Church today, and they will never grow old.

NAME ______________________________

LESSON 23

Compound words

someone

himself

inside

maybe

evergreen

itself

today

themselves

however

throughout

within

myself

something

anything

everywhere

BONUS

candlelight

A compound word is formed by joining two words to form a single word, as in **toothbrush.**

A Sort by Syllable

Divide each list word into two smaller words. Write the first word on the left side of the line, and the second word on the right side.

NAME ______________________________

B Definitions

Below are given definitions to the words found in the list. Write the appropriate word in the space provided next to the definition.

my own identity	1. ________
a thing of any kind	2. ________
in all places	3. ________
having green leaves all year	4. ________
in spite of that	5. ________
an inner side or inner space	6. ________
possibly but not certainly	7. ________
on this day	8. ________
light cast by the flame of a candle	9. ________
through all the parts of	10. ________
inside	11. ________
his own self	12. ________
its own self	13. ________
some person	14. ________
a thing that is not known or named	15. ________
their own selves	16. ________

NAME ______________________

In each sentence below, there is a blank corresponding to one of the words found in the word list. Write the missing word in the space next to the sentence.

Because pine trees are ___, they make good Christmas trees.	1. ________
They are hoping the letter will arrive ___.	2. ________
The horses are ___ the barn.	3. ________
Judas selfishly kept the money for ___.	4. ________
Athletes do stretches to limber ___.	5. ________
Missionaries have preached ___ the world.	6. ________
God is merciful; ___, He is also just.	7. ________
We don't know for sure, but ___ our church will soon be able to get new statues.	8. ________
On Easter, the ___ gave a reverent glow in church.	9. ________
It seemed that ___ we looked, we saw ants!	10. ________
My sister said she did not have ___ to wear to the party.	11. ________
The snake wrapped ___ into a coil.	12. ________
___ removed the holy cards from the desk.	13. ________
Because I am allergic to peanuts, I did not take any of the candies for ___.	14. ________
Mary Magdalen saw the angel ___ the tomb.	15. ________
___ was put in this ice cream to make it green!	16. ________

NAME ______________________________

D Story Time

Read the following story, paying attention to the underlined words. Notice how they use the spelling rule to the right.

A compound word is formed by joining two words to form a single word.

Solomon's Wisdom

David pronounced his last words to his son Solomon, "Take courage, show yourself a man. If you keep God's laws, God will keep His promise which He made to me, that my family should rule Israel forever."

One night, King Solomon offered sacrifice to God, and He was pleased with Solomon. In a dream, He voiced His satisfaction, and told Solomon he would receive anything he wished. Instead of money, Solomon asked for wisdom, so he could rule his nation well. This unselfish request greatly pleased God.

One day, two women came before King Solomon. They were quarreling over a baby. The child of one of the women had died, but each claimed the living child as her own. Solomon found a simple way to settle the point. Taking a sword, he prepared himself to split the baby in half between the mothers.

One mother thought this was fair. However, the other screamed loudly in protest, "Don't kill my baby! Give him to her!"

Solomon saw by her love for the child that she was the real mother, and commanded that the infant be returned to her.

King Solomon finds out who is the mother of the baby.

King Solomon honors an iron worker whose tools helped build the Temple.

NAME ____________________

LESSON 24

Prefixes

complete
explain
behind
distance
beside
contain
present
express
compare
became
insects
process
expect
exceptional
become

BONUS

increase

A prefix is a word part having its own meaning. It is at the beginning of a word. It is usually a separate syllable.

A Sort by Syllable

Sort the words by the prefix listed in the left column.

be	____________________ ____________________ ____________________ ____________________
com	____________________ ____________________
con	____________________
dis	____________________
ex	____________________ ____________________ ____________________ ____________________
in	____________________ ____________________
pre	____________________
pro	____________________

NAME ______________________________

B Definitions

Below are given definitions to the words found in the list. Write the appropriate word in the space provided next to the definition.

in back of	1. ____________
came to be	2. ____________
come to be	3. ____________
by the side of	4. ____________
outstanding; superior	5. ____________
to believe that something will occur	6. ____________
to make clear	7. ____________
to make known in words	8. ____________
a gift	9. ____________
a series of actions leading to some result	10. ____________
to examine for likenesses	11. ____________
entire	12. ____________
to hold	13. ____________
space between two things	14. ____________
to make greater	15. ____________
animals having six legs and three body parts	16. ____________

NAME ______________________

In each sentence below, there is a blank corresponding to one of the words found in the word list. Write the missing word in the space next to the sentence.

We ___ that Father will return from his vacation soon.	1. __________
My dog likes to be scratched ___ the ears.	2. __________
Mother said that Billy was ___ in doing his job.	3. __________
How can you ___ an apple with ice cream?	4. __________
The chalice will soon ___ the Blood of Christ!	5. __________
At Mass, the wine ___ the Blood of Christ.	6. __________
Ann is hoping to ___ a missionary sister.	7. __________
Tommy asked Dad to ___ his allowance.	8. __________
Making the pizza turned out to be a long ___.	9. __________
Can you ___ how the dog got out of the yard?	10. __________
Everyone brought the sick girl a ___.	11. __________
St. Dismas, the good thief, was crucified ___ Our Lord.	12. __________
St. Mary Magdalen made a ___ rejection of her sinful life.	13. __________
It is hard for the little foreign boy to ___ himself clearly.	14. __________
My brother studied ___ in his biology class.	15. __________
The church is only a short ___ from our house.	16. __________

NAME ______________________________

D Story Time

Read the following story, paying attention to the underlined words. Notice how they use the spelling rule to the right.

A prefix is a word part having its own meaning. It is at the beginning of a word.

Solomon's Folly

Solomon began his days as a ruler in complete keeping with God's Laws. By his wisdom and justice, Israel became a great nation. Israel was famous in all the foreign countries. Other kings came to see Solomon for his wisdom. He made his country exceptionally rich and beautiful. He built a great Temple for God.

However, this glory did not last. Toward the end of his life, Solomon became a cruel king. He increased the taxes and forced the people to work for him, both in the city and in his army. This explains why the people were poor and unhappy. His wives did not believe in the One True God. Solomon even presented sacrifices to false gods. Shockingly, Solomon built temples for the false gods at a short distance from Solomon's palace.

This made God very angry. Therefore, God explained to Solomon that Israel would be divided. Solomon's sins were the cause of this punishment. However, because God loved Solomon's father, King David, two tribes would remain under the rule of David's family.

NAME ______________________

LESSON 25

Suffixes

pleasing
helpful
carefully
happiness
quickly
branches
freshest
direction
exciting
acceptance
burning
traveler
action
questions
dependable

BONUS

rested

A suffix is a word part at the end of a word. It is usually a separate syllable. The suffix **-able** is two separate syllables.

A Sort by Syllable

Sort the words by the suffix listed in the left column.

able	______________
ance	______________
ed	______________
er	______________
es	______________
est	______________
ful	______________
ing	______________ ______________ ______________
ion	______________ ______________
ly	______________ ______________
ness	______________
s	______________

NAME ______________________________

B Definitions

Below are given definitions to the words found in the list. Write the appropriate word in the space provided next to the definition.

the doing of something	1. ________
things that are asked	2. ________
producing excitement; thrilling	3. ________
being on fire	4. ________
way; for example, north, south, east, west	5. ________
one who journeys	6. ________
the state or quality of being accepted	7. ________
trustworthy; reliable	8. ________
the most fresh	9. ________
providing help or being of service	10. ________
limbs of a tree	11. ________
the state of being happy	12. ________
doing with care	13. ________
swiftly	14. ________
been refreshed by freedom from activity or work	15. ________
causing delight	16. ________

NAME ______________________________

C Missing Words

In each sentence below, there is a blank corresponding to one of the words found in the word list. Write the missing word in the space next to the sentence.

Consider if your ___ is pleasing to God.	1. ____________
Laura ___ grabbed the falling prayer book.	2. ____________
We go to the dairy to buy the ___ milk.	3. ____________
The bus was going in the wrong ___.	4. ____________
News of the circus was ___ to the boys.	5. ____________
The ___ slept at the inn.	6. ____________
Jesus refused to respond to Herod's ___.	7. ____________
Tom received a letter of ___ from the seminary.	8. ____________
The mover ___ packed Father Burns' vestments.	9. ____________
There was no way Father Vincent could have ___ at the hospital; he had too much to do.	10. ____________
St. Therese's face shone with ___ as she entered the convent.	11. ____________
All the ___ on the tree were filled with apples.	12. ____________
Jessica proved that she was ___ by doing the chores without being told.	13. ____________
The little girl wanted to be ___ to her dad.	14. ____________
Jesus was always ___ to Mary and Joseph.	15. ____________
Moses approached the ___ bush slowly.	16. ____________

NAME ______________________

D Story Time

Read the following story, paying attention to the underlined words. Notice how they use the spelling rule to the right.

A suffix is a word part at the end of a word.

The Division of the Kingdom

After King Solomon died, his son Rehoboam set out to make the people pay higher taxes and work harder than ever before. This news made the people angry, and they revolted. Ten tribes of the north pulled away and set up their own kingdom. They called their country Israel. Two southern tribes stayed faithful to the House of David and Rehoboam. David's grandson ruled over them. This kingdom, called Judah, was small, but the important city of Jerusalem and David's home town of Bethlehem were located in it.

As the years went by, God's people, the Children of Israel, looked away from God to find earthly happiness. Many of the kings, both of Israel and Judah, worshiped pagan gods and committed crimes against God and man. Whenever a king sinned, God would send a prophet to tell the king that God was angry. This did not suit the kings, and they did not always listen. These countries would be punished for their disobedience.

King Solomon and the Queen of Sheba

DAVID'S SON ABSALOM IS HANGED BY HIS LONG HAIR.

NAME

LESSON 26

Consonant with short vowel

second
figure
copy
travel
value
quiver
natural
pedal
seven
visit
energy
finished
level
melody
body

BONUS

petals

When there is a single consonant between two vowels, divide the word after the consonant if the first vowel is short, as in **cab-in, mag-ic, pal-ace.**

A Sort by Syllable

Sort and write the words by the number of syllables.

2	
3	

NAME ____________________

B Definitions

Below are given definitions to the words found in the list. Write the appropriate word in the space provided next to the definition.

the physical part of a person	1. ________
ability to be active	2. ________
to calculate using numbers	3. ________
brought to an end; ate the last part	4. ________
a floor of a building	5. ________
musical sounds in an agreeable arrangement	6. ________
a lever pushed by the foot	7. ________
formed by nature	8. ________
a brief stay	9. ________
one more than six	10. ________
to journey; to move from place to place	11. ________
a duplicate	12. ________
the one after the first	13. ________
worth, usefulness, or importance	14. ________
the colored leaves of a flower	15. ________
to shake	16. ________

NAME ______________________________

In each sentence below, there is a blank corresponding to one of the words found in the word list. Write the missing word in the space next to the sentence.

Diamonds are a ___ resource of South Africa.	1. ____________
The Catholic Church has ___ Sacraments.	2. ____________
Mary went to ___ her cousin Elizabeth.	3. ____________
Who ___ the last piece of cake?	4. ____________
The elevator brought us to the next ___.	5. ____________
Our Lord's lifeless ___ hung on the Cross.	6. ____________
The kitten started to ___ when I picked it up.	7. ____________
The nuns' ___ in helping the poor seemed endless.	8. ____________
Father Ryan said he would say the ___ Mass of the day at 12:00 noon.	9. ____________
Catholics place great importance and ___ on sacred relics.	10. ____________
The priests wanted a ___ of the cardinal's speech.	11. ____________
The missionary priests were required to ___ many miles.	12. ____________
Amy loved to ___ the math answers by herself.	13. ____________
Nick's bicycle was useless without its left ___.	14. ____________
The beautiful ___ of "Ave Maria" made my grandmother cry.	15. ____________
The flower girls threw the rose ___ in front of the bride.	16. ____________

NAME ______________________________

D Story Time

Read the following story, paying attention to the underlined words. Notice how they use the spelling rule to the right.

When there is a single consonant between two vowels, divide the word after the consonant if the first vowel is short.

Man's Need for God

God chose the people of Israel to fill a special place in His Divine Plan. It was from the Jews that His Son was to be born. Therefore, God took great care in telling them about Himself, commanding them to obey His Laws, and teaching them how to do what is right and just.

Even though the Jews knew all this, they sometimes tried to forget it. They thought it would be better to do what they wanted, instead of what God wanted. Because His Laws did not appeal to them, it was simpler to follow their own wills. They trusted themselves rather than God.

When the Jews did this, things did not go as they had planned. Terrible things happened. The three kings of the whole kingdom of Israel are an example. When Saul no longer trusted in God, his people were no longer devoted to him. David sinned, and God punished him when his own son rebelled against him. Solomon turned to false gods, and he was punished by the disharmony in his kingdom and the promise that it would be divided. This trouble could have been avoided. The kings of Israel show us how much we need God.

NAME

Lesson Review

Lesson 19	Lesson 20	Lesson 21	Lesson 22
stretched	lemon	final	third
happened	burden	human	march
printed	sudden	legal	your
filled	kingdom	metal	point
entered	towel	poem	serve
joined	lawful	mental	voice
agreed	medium	total	large
located	mortal	medal	there
received	willful	equal	start
lifted	missal	ankle	terms
resulted	sinful	local	sharp
measured	normal	marvel	chart
covered	fashion	moral	birds
smiled	passion	major	where
picked	parrot	factor	solve
BONUS	BONUS	BONUS	BONUS
reached	awake	ability	first

NAME

Tips from your *Guardian Angel*

- Pronounce each word for correct spelling.
- Say the word, spell it, and say it again.
- Divide each word into syllables.
- Take an oral pretest of all these words, then write each misspelled word three times.

Lesson 23	Lesson 24	Lesson 25	Lesson 26
someone	complete	pleasing	second
himself	explain	helpful	figure
inside	behind	carefully	copy
maybe	distance	happiness	travel
evergreen	beside	quickly	value
itself	contain	branches	quiver
today	present	freshest	natural
themselves	express	direction	pedal
however	compare	exciting	seven
throughout	became	acceptance	visit
within	insects	burning	energy
myself	process	traveler	finished
something	expect	action	level
anything	exceptional	questions	melody
everywhere	become	dependable	body
BONUS	BONUS	BONUS	BONUS
candlelight	increase	rested	petals

J.M.J.

Jesus, Mary, Joseph, I love You. Save souls!

LESSON

28

Consonant with long vowel

humorous

focus

hazel

broken

details

lady

baby

region

meters

later

maple

famous

hero

moment

believe

BONUS

radioactive

NAME ______________________

When there is a single consonant between two vowels, divide the word before the consonant if the first vowel is long, as in **mu-sic, ho-ly, la-dy.**

A Sort by Syllable

Sort and write the words by the number of syllables, then divide them into syllables.

2	______________________ (13 lines)
3	______________________
5	______________________

NAME ______________________________

B Definitions

Below are given definitions to the words found in the list. Write the appropriate word in the space provided next to the definition.

very young child	1. ________
shattered into pieces; fractured	2. ________
a very brief time	3. ________
individual parts; particulars	4. ________
very well-known	5. ________
woman	6. ________
after the usual or present time	7. ________
tree with sweet sap	8. ________
an area without definite boundaries	9. ________
one who shows great courage	10. ________
basic units of length in the metric system, each equal to about a yard	11. ________
giving off radiation, a kind of energy that comes from tiny particles in things	12. ________
to concentrate the eyes	13. ________
a light brown color	14. ________
funny; full of humor	15. ________
to accept as true	16. ________

NAME ______________________________

In each sentence below, there is a blank corresponding to one of the words found in the word list. Write the missing word in the space next to the sentence.

The town council is renaming the street after the war ___.	1. ______________
Mom says our baby's eyes are ___, a light brown.	2. ______________
Jesus' legs were not ___ by the soldiers.	3. ______________
The family prayed to have another ___.	4. ______________
Paul dashed out the door the ___ he heard Dad coming.	5. ______________
How many ___ are in 2 kilometers?	6. ______________
The scientist was not sure if the metal was ___.	7. ______________
Our homeschool group learned how to tap ___ trees and make syrup.	8. ______________
There are many ___ religious paintings in the Vatican.	9. ______________
Thomas would not ___ Jesus had risen from the dead.	10. ______________
Matthew could not remember all the ___ about the accident.	11. ______________
The eye doctor asked me to ___ on the eye chart.	12. ______________
Mom and Dad did not want to make the decision until ___.	13. ______________
James helped the elderly ___ by carrying her groceries.	14. ______________
Our town is in the northern ___ of the state.	15. ______________
My uncle Kevin told us a very ___ bedtime story.	16. ______________

NAME ______________________________

D Story Time

Read the following story, paying attention to the underlined words. Notice how they use the spelling rule to the right.

> When there is a single consonant between two vowels, divide the word before the consonant if the first vowel is long.

God Against Baal

In the northern kingdom of Israel, men quickly forgot about the true God and began to believe in false gods. Even the king of Israel did this.

One day, a prophet came to King Ahaz's court. His name was Elijah. He spoke to the king, telling him that God would no longer send rain to the land, and it happened as He promised. God was punishing Israel for worshiping idols. This lasted for three-and-a-half years.

Later, Elijah returned. He told the king that it was his sins that caused Israel's trouble. Then he had the king gather the priests of the pagan "god," Baal, to offer sacrifice, and Elijah would offer sacrifice to the one true God. The real God would show His acceptance of the sacrifice by causing it to burn by a fire from Heaven.

The priests of Baal readied the sacrifice and tried in every way they could think of to get their "god's" attention. They danced and screamed, and cut themselves with knives. But since Baal didn't really exist, nothing happened.

Then Elijah said a simple prayer to God, and his sacrifice was immediately struck by lightning and burned. In amazement, everyone bowed down and worshiped the one true God.

Elijah warns the king that his sins caused Israel's troubles.

Isaias was one of the greatest Old Testament prophets.

J.M.J.

Jesus, Mary, Joseph, I love You. Save souls!

NAME ______________________________

LESSON 29

Two consonants

happy
button
center
puddle
pretty
captain
better
effect
appear
marry
ferry
engine
valley
army
basket

BONUS

merry

When two or more consonants come between two vowels, divide the word between the first two consonants, as in **cus-tom.**

A Sort by Syllable

Sort and write the words by the accented vowel sounds.

a	______________________
	______________________
	______________________
	______________________
	______________________
	______________________
e	______________________
	______________________
	______________________
	______________________
	______________________
	______________________
	______________________
ea	______________________
u	______________________
	______________________

NAME ______________________________

B Definitions

Below are given definitions to the words found in the list. Write the appropriate word in the space provided next to the definition.

Definition	
an area of land between hills or mountains	1. ________
a container usually made of woven materials	2. ________
very small pool, usually of muddy water	3. ________
to come into sight	4. ________
the military forces of a nation trained for land warfare	5. ________
a small object used for fastening	6. ________
more satisfactory than another	7. ________
one in command; leader	8. ________
the middle part of a circle or object	9. ________
result; consequence	10. ________
a machine for driving or operating something	11. ________
a boat used to carry persons over a small body of water	12. ________
join as husband and wife	13. ________
having a good feeling	14. ________
a word for joyful or cheerful, usually used in Christmas greetings	15. ________
attractive	16. ________

NAME ____________________

In each sentence below, there is a blank corresponding to one of the words found in the word list. Write the missing word in the space next to the sentence.

My brother played in the ___ of water.	1. ____________
What ___ will this storm have on my farm crops?	2. ____________
Mary will ___ on stage tonight.	3. ____________
Dad's new truck has a huge ___.	4. ____________
That painting would look ___ with a blue sky.	5. ____________
The ___ conducted a search mission in the jungle.	6. ____________
We visited the shrine in the beautiful Shenandoah ___.	7. ____________
The girls thought the new pearl rosary was very ___.	8. ____________
Sally lost the big red ___ that was on her coat.	9. ____________
The priest waited in the ___ of the sanctuary for the altar boys.	10. ____________
The ___ of the ship attended daily Mass.	11. ____________
Father Jones instructed couples who wanted to ___.	12. ____________
The children sang ___ Christmas to the retired nuns.	13. ____________
My family took the ___ out to Kelly's Island.	14. ____________
The bishop was ___ that we knew our catechism.	15. ____________
St. Paul was lowered over the wall in a ___.	16. ____________

NAME ______________________________

D Story Time

Read the following story, paying attention to the underlined words. Notice how they use the spelling rule to the right.

> When two or more consonants come between two vowels, divide the word between the first two consonants.

The Prophets

When the people of Israel and Judah no longer obeyed God, He'd send men to warn them that their sins offended Him. These men were called prophets.

These men didn't care for money or comfort, and they spent their whole time praying, fasting, and studying God's Laws. They were God's way of speaking to a sinful people, to keep the Faith alive in the hearts of at least a few. Some of the prophets wrote down almost everything important that happened in Israel and Judah. It is from these writings, which are part of the Bible, that we know the history of those times. Some of them also wrote what God showed in visions, telling what would come to pass many years later. God sent the prophets mainly to teach the people the Ten Commandments.

Isaias was one of the greatest prophets. He lived when the land of Judah was filled with men who constantly sinned against God. He preached to everyone, the kings and the people. He scolded them for their wickedness, and he told them what God wanted of them.

NAME ____________________

LESSON 30

The separate vowel

iron
open
ahead
creation
marinate
ocean
area
monument
alone
various
capital
able
capitol
afraid
against

BONUS

oxygen

If a vowel is sounded separately in a word, divide before and after that vowel, as in **hes-i-tate, pal-i-sade**; divide after that vowel when it begins the word, as in **e-quip, a-lert, o-bey.**

A Sort by Syllable

Sort and write the words by the number of syllables.

2	____________________ ____________________ ____________________ ____________________ ____________________ ____________________ ____________________ ____________________
3	____________________ ____________________ ____________________ ____________________ ____________________ ____________________ ____________________ ____________________

NAME ______________________

B Definitions

Below are given definitions to the words found in the list. Write the appropriate word in the space provided next to the definition.

capable of	1. ______
filled with fear	2. ______
in contact with; pressing on	3. ______
in front	4. ______
not including anyone else; by oneself	5. ______
allowing entry; not shut or closed	6. ______
object to smooth out wrinkles; a heavy metallic element that rusts easily	7. ______
large body of sea water	8. ______
a surface or space	9. ______
something that serves as a memorial, such as a pillar or stone	10. ______
to soak food in a flavorful sauce	11. ______
the act of bringing the world into existence out of nothing	12. ______
a city where the government of a state or country is located	13. ______
the building in which a government's lawmakers meet	14. ______
many and different	15. ______
odorless gas necessary for breathing	16. ______

NAME ______________________________

In each sentence below, there is a blank corresponding to one of the words found in the word list. Write the missing word in the space next to the sentence.

___ is in the air we breathe.	1. ______
Mom told us not to leave the windows ___ when the air conditioner is running.	2. ______
The shrine included an ___ for the Stations of the Cross.	3. ______
Mark leaned his bike ___ the wall.	4. ______
Dad likes to ___ the steaks before he grills them.	5. ______
The apostles were ___ before the Holy Spirit came to them.	6. ______
We visited the delegates in the state ___ building.	7. ______
The ___ city in our state has a very large cathedral.	8. ______
Grandmother was not ___ to visit us this week.	9. ______
We visited the Washington ___ in Washington, D. C.	10. ______
Mother could not find the ___ to smooth out the wrinkles in my skirt.	11. ______
John ran ___ of Peter to the tomb.	12. ______
Mary stood all ___ in the empty room.	13. ______
Dad told the boys the story of God's ___.	14. ______
Columbus sailed across the ___ to discover America.	15. ______
There were ___ reasons why the boys did not go swimming.	16. ______

NAME

D Story Time

Read the following story, paying attention to the underlined words. Notice how they use the spelling rule to the right.

If a vowel is sounded separately in a word, divide before and after that vowel; divide after that vowel when it begins the word.

Jonah

Israel and Judah were the only countries where God revealed Himself to His people, but He still cared for the other nations, even though they did not know about Him or serve Him. This is why God sent the prophet Jonah to the Ninevites. He told him to tell the people to repent, or in forty days, He would destroy the city.

Jonah didn't want to do this because Nineveh was the capital city of the Assyrians, the enemy of Judah. So instead of obeying God, he ran away. He boarded a ship that was heading in the other direction.

While on the ship, a great storm came up that made the sailors believe that the ship would sink. They woke Jonah and begged him to pray, or they would all drown. Jonah knew that it was his fault, so he told them to throw him in the water to make the storm stop. The sailors did as he told them, and the sea grew calm.

Jonah did not drown in the water. God sent a huge fish which swallowed him. God kept Jonah alive for three days, then made the fish spit him out on dry land.

Now Jonah obeyed God. He warned the Ninevites what would happen if they did not repent, and they believed him. They turned from their evil ways and began to pray. Even the king did penance. So it happened that God had mercy on them, and Nineveh was saved.

Jonah is thrown to the whale.

Tobias cures his father's blindness.

NAME ______________________________

LESSON 31

-le words

simple
uncle
cattle
syllable
double
parable
trouble
sparkle
tabernacle
scribble
angle
settle
apple
miracle
ample

BONUS

single

When **le** preceded by a consonant comes at the end of a word, the consonant and **le** form a separate syllable. Divide the word before the consonant, as in **rat-tle, bu-gle, bri-dle.**

A Sort by Syllable

Sort and write the words by the number of syllables.

2	______________________________
	______________________________
	______________________________
	______________________________
	______________________________
	______________________________
	______________________________
	______________________________
	______________________________
	______________________________
	______________________________
	______________________________
3	______________________________
	______________________________
	______________________________
4	______________________________

NAME ______________________

B Definitions

Below are given definitions to the words found in the list. Write the appropriate word in the space provided next to the definition.

the figure formed when two lines or planes meet	1. ______
fruit with red, green, or yellow skin	2. ______
more than enough; plenty	3. ______
cows	4. ______
an extraordinary event taken as a sign of the power of God	5. ______
a simple story that teaches a moral truth	6. ______
place so as to stay; decide	7. ______
not fancy; easy to understand	8. ______
one only	9. ______
letters in a word representing one unit of sound; a part of a word	10. ______
something that is twice another	11. ______
problem; difficulty	12. ______
the brother of one's father or mother	13. ______
to give off small flashes of light	14. ______
to cover with meaningless marks	15. ______
the place on the high altar in which the Blessed Sacrament is kept	16. ______

NAME ____________________

In each sentence below, there is a blank corresponding to one of the words found in the word list. Write the missing word in the space next to the sentence.

Dad's brother, my ___, was ordained last week.	1. ____________
Jesus told a ___ about a rich man.	2. ____________
The Blessed Sacrament is reserved in the ___.	3. ____________
King Solomon was able to ___ the debate.	4. ____________
Healing the blind man was a ___.	5. ____________
We often ask Mother to make us an ___ pie.	6. ____________
There was ___ time for the Rosary before dinner.	7. ____________
St. Joseph of Cupertino was always getting into ___.	8. ____________
My baby sister tried to ___ on the wall.	9. ____________
Little Joe could read only words of one ___.	10. ____________
The rancher took care of a large herd of ___.	11. ____________
My uncle asked for a ___ helping of chocolate ice cream.	12. ____________
Mother's wedding ring would ___ in the sunlight.	13. ____________
The pastor said a short and ___ prayer for my grandfather.	14. ____________
The men were able to paint the church hall in a ___ day.	15. ____________
An ___ that makes a square corner is called a right angle.	16. ____________

NAME

D Story Time

Read the following story, paying attention to the underlined words. Notice how they use the spelling rule to the right.

When **le** preceded by a consonant comes at the end of a word, the consonant and **le** form a separate syllable.

Tobias and the Angel

When the kingdoms of Israel and Judah were divided, Assyria was the most powerful country in the world. They conquered parts of Israel and took many of the Israelites as prisoners. Among these was a good and pious man named Tobias, who, along with his family and many others, was made to live in the capital city of Nineveh.

Even though Tobias was no longer <u>able</u> to go to the <u>Temple</u> to adore God and offer his gifts, he still prayed and studied God's Laws, and tried to help and comfort everyone he knew among the Hebrew prisoners in Nineveh. Besides the many other <u>troubles</u> Tobias endured, he was also stricken blind.

Tobias had a son, who was also good and pious, who was named after his father. His father sent him on a long journey to collect some money that a friend owed him. Young Tobias started out rather worried. He did not know the way, nor the friend who owed them the money, and traveling was dangerous. However, a friendly young man offered to be his guide.

The guide took Tobias to the end of his journey and collected the money for him. In addition, the guide found him a wife who was both good and beautiful, and also an Israelite. The guide brought back young Tobias and his wife, safe and happy, to <u>settle</u> them in the family home in Nineveh. Since young Tobias had trusted in Him, God blessed the elder Tobias with a <u>miracle</u>, curing him of his blindness.

When Tobias tried to pay the guide for his help, he told them that he was Raphael, one of the angels of God. He was sent to help them because of their prayers and good works. Their <u>troubles</u> had been sent to test them.

NAME ____________________

LESSON 32

Two vowels with separate sounds

museum
manual
diagonal
scientists
create
fiesta
idea
violin
quietly
giant
lion
being
piano
dual
diet

BONUS

science

When two vowels come together within the same word, but each vowel has a separate sound, the syllables are divided between the two vowels, as in **cre-ate, sci-ence, fi-es-ta**.

A Sort by Syllable

Sort and write the words by the number of syllables.

2	______ ______ ______ ______ ______ ______ ______
3	______ ______ ______ ______ ______ ______ ______ ______
4	______

NAME ____________________

B Definitions

Below are given definitions to the words found in the list. Write the appropriate word in the space provided next to the definition.

form of the verb *be*	1. ________
to cause to exist; to make from nothing	2. ________
with a minimum of noise or activity	3. ________
a branch of knowledge about the physical world	4. ________
keyboard instrument	5. ________
those who study science or do scientific work	6. ________
a slanted line	7. ________
a handbook	8. ________
a stringed instrument held under the chin and played with a bow	9. ________
very great in size	10. ________
of or having two parts; double	11. ________
a festival or religious celebration in nations where Spanish is spoken	12. ________
any thought, belief, picture, or image formed in the mind	13. ________
a large, powerful animal in the cat family, with short, beige fur	14. ________
a building where collections of important objects are kept and shown to the public	15. ________
the food and drink a person usually eats and drinks	16. ________

J.M.J.

Jesus, Mary, Joseph, I love You. Save souls!

NAME ______________________

In each sentence below, there is a blank corresponding to one of the words found in the word list. Write the missing word in the space next to the sentence.

Leonardo da Vinci's famous painting, the Mona Lisa, is kept in the Louvre, an art ___ in Paris.	1. ______________
The Mexicans throw a huge ___ on December 12, in honor of Our Lady of Guadalupe.	2. ______________
Mike is so creative! I'm sure he has a good ___ of what we should do.	3. ______________
Andrew ought to replace the missing string on his ___.	4. ______________
We ___ tiptoed while the baby was sleeping.	5. ______________
The ___ is called the king of beasts.	6. ______________
Dad said that two of us could take ___ lessons.	7. ______________
Martin's project won first prize at the ___ fair.	8. ______________
Doctors have learned that ___ happy also means being healthy.	9. ______________
Poor Jimmy's tummy was so full that he wished he hadn't eaten the ___ burger.	10. ______________
Katie soon realized her steady ___ of candy and snack foods was bad for her health.	11. ______________
Dave built the model railroad by following the directions in the ___.	12. ______________
Hats serve the ___ purpose of warming the head and making the wearer look well-dressed.	13. ______________
Only God can ___ out of nothing.	14. ______________
Uncle Tom said that ___ are still learning about outer space.	15. ______________
A ___ line in a rectangle makes two triangles.	16. ______________

NAME

D Story Time

Read the following story, paying attention to the underlined words. Notice how they use the spelling rule to the right.

When one vowel follows another within a word, but each vowel has a separate sound, the syllables are divided between the two vowels.

Job

Once there was a very good man whose name was Job. He was very wealthy and everyone respected him. God was very pleased with this holy man and his quiet faithfulness.

Some people believed that Job was a holy man only because he had such an easy life, so God permitted Job to be tested. First, robbers stole all of his cattle and belongings, and then a giant storm came that killed all of his sons and daughters, who were feasting together in the same house. Then Job became extremely ill. He had boils all over his body, and the pain was so great that he could neither eat nor sleep. All this happened very quickly.

Through all this, Job remained faithful to the mighty God. He said that if God gave him good things, He could give him bad things also, if He wanted. Job was being completely faithful to God.

Then three of Job's friends came to visit him. They had somehow gotten the idea that his great suffering must be the result of a very serious sin, but Job said no. Though he did sin in small ways like everyone else, he knew he was not generally wicked.

At last, God said to Job and his friends, "Surely, you cannot expect to understand My ways, nor can you know why Job suffers. I am angry with you who have offended Job, who has remained faithful to Me. But if he will pray for you, I will forgive you."

Then God rapidly cured Job of his sickness. He once again enjoyed manual labor. God gave him twice as many cattle, sheep, and donkeys as he had before. God also gave him ten more children, and his daughters were the most beautiful and virtuous girls in the whole world.

Job tells his friends that he is not wicked.

THE HEBREWS ARE MARCHED AWAY TO LIVE IN CAPTIVITY.

LESSON 33

Spelling strategies

president
everyone
understand
discovered
estimate
electric
underline
exactly
separate
repeated
everything
represent
suddenly
suggested
especially

BONUS

decided

NAME ______________________

Learn to spell correctly by applying spelling rules and patterns rather than by relying solely on your memory.

A Sort by Syllable

Sort and write the words by the number of syllables.

3	____ ____ ____ ____ ____ ____ ____ ____ ____ ____ ____ ____ ____ ____ ____
4	____

NAME ______________________________

B Definitions

Below are given definitions to the words found in the list. Write the appropriate word in the space provided next to the definition.

Definition	
made a choice	1. __________
to know thoroughly	2. __________
found out for the first time	3. __________
in particular	4. __________
the head of a government or organization	5. __________
relating to electricity	6. __________
accurately; correctly; precisely	7. __________
every person	8. __________
recommended	9. __________
to draw a line under	10. __________
to pull apart	11. __________
told again	12. __________
to make a careful guess about the amount, size, or worth of	13. __________
all things	14. __________
to act for or in place of	15. __________
hastily, quickly, swiftly	16. __________

NAME ______________________

C Missing Words

In each sentence below, there is a blank corresponding to one of the words found in the word list. Write the missing word in the space next to the sentence.

I'm going to invite ___ I know to the Baptism!	1. ______________
The researcher ___ the cause of the sickness.	2. ______________
Father Joseph ___ the same story for the children.	3. ______________
The priest liked to hear confessions, ___ for the children.	4. ______________
The ___ lives in the White House.	5. ______________
The cardinal said he would ___ the pope at the international conference.	6. ______________
The bishop ___ to say Mass in the cathedral.	7. ______________
The nuns ___ that the children give to the poor.	8. ______________
My brother found it easy to ___ the math problems.	9. ______________
I don't know exactly how long the trip will take, but I ___ it will be about five hours.	10. ______________
The ___ train was a favorite with my brothers.	11. ______________
She followed the directions ___ as Sister Agnes told her.	12. ______________
___, Baby Mary started crying!	13. ______________
Tim could not ___ the frozen hamburgers.	14. ______________
Mom said I should ___ the vocabulary words.	15. ______________
I listened to ___ that Father Smith said to us.	16. ______________

NAME ____________________

D Story Time

Read the following story, paying attention to the underlined words. Notice how they use the spelling rule to the right.

Learn to spell correctly by applying spelling rules and patterns.

The Babylonian Captivity

Now that God's people were divided in two, they were much weaker and fought with each other and with outside enemies. No one could understand what was happening. Judah was more faithful to God, but still the inhabitants grew to be so wicked that the Lord sent them attackers from all sides. Finally, Jerusalem itself was taken, the Temple of Solomon was partially torn down, and its treasures taken away to be used in pagan shrines. The people discovered they had lost everything that was important.

The king of Judah and many thousands of the Hebrews were marched away to live as prisoners of war in the enemy country of Babylon. Suddenly, their entire lives were changed. Parents became separated from their children. In Babylon, the Jewish people were slaves. They worked hard and lived poorly. This made them think of all the times they had disobeyed God. They realized that this was a punishment because they were such great sinners. They also saw how dear their God, His Laws, and the land that He gave to them were. It was during this time that they made a special effort to collect all the writings of the prophets and put them together in what is now known as the Old Testament. These writings became especially important, as they represented God's words spoken to His people from the beginning of time.

When God's chosen people were finally allowed to return home, they were no longer a sinful people, but a people ready to do the Will of God. As soon as they returned to Judah, they began to rebuild the Temple, and offer sacrifice to Him, their Protector, Who let them return safely. They discovered once again the joy of obeying God's Commandments.

NAME ______________________

LESSON 34

Spelling strategies

molecules
farmers
industry
together
sentence
determine
remember
indicate
divided
century
information
developed
addition
material
paragraph

BONUS

particular

Learn to spell correctly by applying spelling rules and patterns rather than by relying solely on your memory.

A Sort by Syllable

Sort and write the words by the number of syllables.

2	______________________ ______________________
3	______________________ ______________________ ______________________ ______________________ ______________________ ______________________ ______________________ ______________________ ______________________ ______________________ ______________________
4	______________________ ______________________ ______________________

NAME ______________________________

B Definitions

Below are given definitions to the words found in the list. Write the appropriate word in the space provided next to the definition.

Definition	
the activity of making things to sell	1. ______________
a group of words that make a statement or ask a question	2. ______________
in one group	3. ______________
the smallest portions of a substance	4. ______________
100 years	5. ______________
to decide; to come to a conclusion	6. ______________
keep in or recall to mind	7. ______________
separated into two or more parts	8. ______________
made more usable; brought to a more advanced state	9. ______________
several sentences about one topic	10. ______________
made of matter	11. ______________
a collection of facts	12. ______________
to point out	13. ______________
the adding of numbers	14. ______________
people who work on farms	15. ______________
specific	16. ______________

NAME ____________________

In each sentence below, there is a blank corresponding to one of the words found in the word list. Write the missing word in the space next to the sentence.

"The family that prays ___ stays together."	1. ________
Try to define the word by its use in the ___.	2. ________
___ to give thanks to God for all we have.	3. ________
The colorful rosaries were ___ among the children.	4. ________
In sixteenth ___ England, priests were outlawed.	5. ________
When Mom called the pastor to ask about the catechism class, he gave her all the ___ she needed.	6. ________
A chalice must be made of precious ___, such as gold.	7. ________
Sentences in a ___ must explain the topic sentence.	8. ________
We buy eggs from the ___ in the area.	9. ________
She had no ___ reason for calling her friend.	10. ________
We studied atoms and ___ in science class.	11. ________
The American steel ___ is not as strong as it used to be.	12. ________
My little brother is studying ___ and subtraction.	13. ________
After much thought, I did ___ what to do.	14. ________
The citizens want the waterfront repaired and ___ for use with motorboats and sailboats.	15. ________
Father Brown did not ___ to us who would serve at the late Mass.	16. ________

NAME ______________________________

D Story Time

Read the following story, paying attention to the underlined words. Notice how they use the spelling rule to the right.

Learn to spell correctly by applying spelling rules and patterns.

Eleazar

Judah came under the rule of the king of Syria. This king was named Antiochus. He wanted the Jews to be pagan like the Greeks. He ordered that all the sacred books be burned, and most of the Jews obeyed him in fear. Conflicts among the Jews developed quickly.

Many remembered God's wrath at their past disobedience. They were determined to remain faithful. Among those who refused to disobey God's Law was an old man named Eleazar. Antiochus tried to force him to eat swine meat, which was forbidden to the Jews. When Eleazar refused, Antiochus sentenced him to severe torture.

Some of his friends went together to plead with Eleazar. They did not want to see him tortured or killed for this. They told Eleazar that he should just pretend to eat the forbidden meat while actually eating something that was allowed. They determined that the farmers would bring him food secretly.

Eleazar would not consider this particular plan to fool the enemy. Though it might save him from suffering for a little while, it would do much harm and divide the people, Eleazar said. It would set a bad example for the rest of the Jews, especially for the young people. Even though he might avoid suffering for the moment, he would ultimately have to face God's Judgment for his deception and the scandal it would cause. In addition to the disgrace among his people, Eleazar would also be subject to the displeasure of God.

So, old Eleazar was killed because he remained obedient to God's Laws. He was an Old Testament martyr, a witness to the One True God.

ELEAZAR

Judas Maccabeus

NAME ____________________

LESSON 35

Spelling strategies

laughter
dictionary
consider
diocese
factories
adjective
method
important
exercise
prepared
company
written
triangle
substances
numeral

BONUS

division

Learn to spell correctly by applying spelling rules and patterns rather than by relying solely on your memory.

A Sort by Syllable

Sort and write the words by the number of syllables.

2	____________________ ____________________ ____________________ ____________________
3	____________________ ____________________ ____________________ ____________________ ____________________ ____________________ ____________________ ____________________ ____________________ ____________________ ____________________
4	____________________

NAME ______________________________

B Definitions

Below are given definitions to the words found in the list. Write the appropriate word in the space provided next to the definition.

a certain way of doing something	1. ____________
significant	2. ____________
places where goods are manufactured	3. ____________
number	4. ____________
the region governed by a bishop	5. ____________
book that gives the meaning of words	6. ____________
a figure with three sides	7. ____________
to think over carefully	8. ____________
bodily activity for health	9. ____________
the process of dividing	10. ____________
guests at one's home	11. ____________
the sound of laughing	12. ____________
having letters or words made with pen or pencil	13. ____________
materials; things	14. ____________
to make ready beforehand for some particular reason	15. ____________
a word that describes a noun	16. ____________

NAME ______________________________

In each sentence below, there is a blank corresponding to one of the words found in the word list. Write the missing word in the space next to the sentence.

Use a ___ to look up the meaning of the words.	1. ____________
Our pastor said he would ___ which boys would serve the funeral Mass.	2. ____________
Six men were ordained to the priesthood from our ___.	3. ____________
Proper ___ is important for good health.	4. ____________
Anne ___ all the lunches for the altar boys' field trip.	5. ____________
The baby's sudden ___ made everyone smile.	6. ____________
We are just starting to learn ___ problems in math class.	7. ____________
It is ___ to go to Confession at least once a month.	8. ____________
The new ___ provided jobs for many fathers in town.	9. ____________
A ___ has three angles and three sides.	10. ____________
The Roman ___ for ten is an X.	11. ____________
My music teacher uses a special ___ to teach how to play the violin.	12. ____________
An ___ is a word that describes a noun.	13. ____________
Some chemical ___ are poisonous to animals.	14. ____________
Father Jones said that he needed ___ permission notes from parents.	15. ____________
Mother said that we would have ___ after the Baptism.	16. ____________

NAME ____________________

D Story Time

Read the following story, paying attention to the underlined words. Notice how they use the spelling rule to the right.

Learn to spell correctly by applying spelling rules and patterns.

Judas Maccabeus

Antiochus made it very hard for the Jews to practice their religion. Some, like the aged Eleazar, refused to even consider being disobedient. Among them was another old man named Mattathias. He not only refused to obey Antiochus, but started a rebellion against him. He fled to the mountains with his sons, and many brave men joined them.

When Mattathias died, his son, Judas Maccabeus, led the rebellion and prepared for resistance. Under his leadership, these men fought many important battles against the army of Antiochus. Even though the Greek army was better trained in military methods, God was on the side of the Jews, and He helped them win many battles. By His aid, the Jews were able to recover Jerusalem and its holy Temple.

Judas continued to fight King Antiochus. After very many battles, Judas was killed while still fighting.

NAME

Lesson Review

Lesson 28	Lesson 29	Lesson 30	Lesson 31
humorous	happy	iron	simple
focus	button	open	uncle
hazel	center	ahead	cattle
broken	puddle	creation	syllable
details	pretty	marinate	double
lady	captain	ocean	parable
baby	better	area	trouble
region	effect	monument	sparkle
meters	appear	alone	tabernacle
later	marry	various	scribble
maple	ferry	capital	angle
famous	engine	able	settle
hero	valley	capitol	apple
moment	army	afraid	miracle
believe	basket	against	ample
BONUS	BONUS	BONUS	BONUS
radioactive	merry	oxygen	single

NAME ______________________________

Tips from your *Guardian Angel*

- Pronounce each word for correct spelling.
- Say the word, spell it, and say it again.
- Divide each word into syllables.
- Take an oral pretest of all these words, then write each misspelled word three times.

Lesson 32	Lesson 33	Lesson 34	Lesson 35
museum	president	molecules	laughter
manual	everyone	farmers	dictionary
diagonal	understand	industry	consider
scientists	discovered	together	diocese
create	estimate	sentence	factories
fiesta	electric	determine	adjective
idea	underline	remember	method
violin	exactly	indicate	important
quietly	separate	divided	exercise
giant	repeated	century	prepared
lion	everything	information	company
being	represent	developed	written
piano	suddenly	addition	triangle
dual	suggested	material	substances
diet	especially	paragraph	numeral
BONUS	BONUS	BONUS	BONUS
science	decided	particular	division

Spelling Short Vowel sounds

Vowel Sounds	Common Spelling Patterns	Sample Words	Some Other Spellings
/aa/ in **a**t	**a**	**a**t	**au** (l**au**gh)
/eh/ in **e**gg	**e, ea**	r**e**d, r**ea**d	**ai** (s**ai**d)
/ih/ in **i**t	**i, y, ui**	h**i**m, h**y**mn, b**ui**ld	**ee** (b**ee**n)
/ah/ in **o**x	**o, a**	**o**x, **A**men	**ho** (**ho**nor)
/uh/ in **u**s	**u, ou**	**u**s, t**ou**ch	**o** (s**o**n)

Spelling Long Vowel sounds

Vowel Sounds	Common Spelling Patterns	Sample Words	Some Other Spellings
/ay/ in **a**te	**a, ay, ai, eigh, ey, ea, ei**	**a**te, h**ay**, r**ai**n, **eigh**t, h**ey**, br**ea**k, r**ei**n	**eig** (r**eig**n)
/ee/ in **e**ve	**e, ea, ee, ey, y, i, ie, ei**	**e**ve, s**ea**, s**ee**, k**ey**, hol**y**, p**i**ano, pr**ie**st, rec**ei**ve	**eo** (p**eo**ple)
/iy/ in **i**ce	**i, ie, igh, y, ui**	s**i**te, t**ie**, s**igh**t, b**y**, g**ui**de	**uy** (b**uy**)
/oh/ in **o**ak	**o, ow, ough, oa, oe, oo, ou**	s**o**, gr**ow**n, d**ough**, gr**oa**n, d**oe**, fl**oo**r, f**ou**r	**ew** (s**ew**)
/yoo/ in **u**se	**u, ew, eu**	**u**se, f**ew**, f**eu**d	**eau** (b**eau**ty)

Spelling Other Vowel sounds

Vowel Sounds	Common Spelling Patterns	Sample Words	Some Other Spellings
/aw/ in **awe**	**a, o, aw, au, ough**	c**a**ll, **o**ften, p**aw**, p**au**se, th**ough**t	**augh** (t**augh**t)
/oo/ in **oo**ze	**oo, o, ew, ue, ui, ough, ou, eu**	t**oo**, t**o**, bl**ew**, bl**ue**, fr**ui**t, thr**ough**, gr**ou**p, n**eu**tral	**u** (tr**u**th)
/uu/ in b**oo**k	**oo, u**	w**oo**d, p**u**t	**ou** (w**ou**ld)
/ou/ in **ou**t	**ou, ow**	**ou**t, b**ow**	**ough** (b**ough**)
/oi/ in **oi**l	**oi, oy**	**oi**l, b**oy**	

Spelling Consonant Sounds

Consonant Sounds	Common Spelling Patterns	Sample Words	Some Other Spellings
/b/ in **b**ell	**b**	**b**ell	**bb** (ra**bb**it)
/d/ in **d**a**d**	**d, ed**	**d**a**d**, lov**ed**	**dd** (su**dd**en)
/f/ in **f**an	**f, ph, gh**	**f**an, **ph**one, lau**gh**	**ff** (stu**ff**)
/g/ in **G**od	**g, gh**	**G**od, **gh**ost	**gu** (**gu**ard)
/h/ in **h**at	**h**	**h**ole	**wh** (**wh**ole)
/j/ in **j**am	**j, dge, g**	**j**am, fu**dge**, **g**em	**ge** (ca**ge**)
/k/ in **c**at	**c, ch, ck, k**	**c**at, s**ch**ool, du**ck**, **k**itten	**qu** (mos**qu**ito)
/l/ in **l**amb	**l**	**l**amb	**ll** (ma**ll**)
/m/ in **M**ass	**m**	**M**ass	**mb** (la**mb**)
/n/ in **n**u**n**	**n, kn, gn**	**n**o, **kn**ow, **gn**at	**pn** (**pn**eumonia)
/p/ in **p**et	**p**	**p**et	**pp** (ha**pp**en)
/kw/ in **qu**een	**qu**	**qu**een	
/r/ in **r**un	**r, wr**	**r**ight, **wr**ite	**rh** (**rh**yme)
/s/ in **s**at	**s, c, sc**	**s**ent, **c**ent, **sc**ent	**ss** (Ma**ss**)
/t/ in **t**op	**t, ed**	**t**op, fix**ed**	**tt** (ki**tt**en)
/v/ in **v**an	**v**	**v**an	**f** (o**f**)
/w/ in **w**ise	**w, wh**	**w**on, **wh**ale	**o** (**o**ne)
/ks/ in bo**x**	**x**	bo**x**	
/y/ in **y**es	**y**	**y**es	**i** (on**i**on)
/z/ in **z**oo	**z, s**	**z**oo, i**s**	**x** (**x**ylophone)
/ch/ in **ch**ur**ch**	**ch, tch**	**ch**ur**ch**, wa**tch**	**ti** (ques**ti**on)
/ng/ in si**ng**	**ng**	si**ng**	**n** (si**n**k)
/sh/ in **sh**eep	**sh, ti, si, ci, ch**	**sh**eep, frac**ti**on, mis**si**on, spe**ci**al, ma**ch**ine	**ce** (o**ce**an)
/th/ in **th**is	**th**	**th**is	
/th/ in **th**in	**th**	**th**in	
/zh/ in vi**si**on	**si, ti**	vi**si**on, equa**ti**on	**s** (u**s**ual)

Spelling Rules for Consonants

The **/kw/** sound is spelled with the two letters **q** and **u**, as in **qu**iet. The letter **q** is always followed by the letter **u**.

The **/l/**, **/f/**, and **/s/** sounds after a single vowel in one-syllable words are often spelled **ll**, **ff**, and **ss**, as in be**ll**, stu**ff**, and Ma**ss**.

The **/k/** sound after a short vowel is spelled **ck**, as in qua**ck**, ne**ck**, qui**ck**, clo**ck**, and du**ck**.

The **/j/** sound after a short vowel is spelled **dge**, as in ba**dge**, ple**dge**, bri**dge**, do**dge**, and fu**dge**.

The **/z/** sound in **z**oo at the beginning of a root word is usually spelled **z** and never spelled **s**.

The **/sh/** sound at the beginning of a word or at the end of a syllable is usually spelled **sh**, as in **sh**eep and wi**sh**. At the beginning of any syllable after the first one, the **/sh/** sound is usually spelled **ti**, **si**, or **ci**, (except for the ending **-ship**, as in friend**ship**), as in frac**ti**on, man**si**on, and spe**ci**al. When the syllable before it ends in **s**, as in mis**si**on, it is spelled **si**.

All, **till**, and **full** are usually spelled with one **l** when they are added to another syllable, as in **al**most, un**til**, and care**ful**.

The **/v/** sound at the end of a word is never spelled **v**. It is usually spelled **ve**, as in ha**ve**.

Spelling Rules for Vowels

The **/iy/** sound is not spelled **i** at the end of most words.

The **/ay/** sound is not spelled **a** at the end of root words.

The **/ee/** sound after **c** is spelled **ei**, as in rec**ei**ve.

Phonics Rules for Consonants

The letter **c** before **e**, **i**, or **y** makes the **/s/** sound, as in **c**ent, **c**ity, and **c**ycle. It makes the **/k/** sound before **a**, **o**, and **u**, as in **c**at, **c**old, and **c**up.

The letter **g** before **e**, **i**, or **y** sometimes makes the **/j/** sound, as in **g**em, **g**iant, and **g**ym. It usually makes the **/g/** sound before **a**, **o**, and **u**, as in **g**ame, **G**od, and **g**um.

The letters **si** between two vowels can make the **/zh/** sound, as in vi**si**on.

Phonics Rules for Vowels

The vowels **a**, **e**, **o**, and **u** at the end of a syllable usually make the long vowel sounds **/ay/**, **/ee/**, **/oh/**, or **/yoo/**, as in p**a**per, b**e**gin, **o**pen, and **u**nit.

The vowels **i** and **o** often make the long vowel sounds **/iy/** and **/oh/** when followed by two consonants, as in k**i**nd and g**o**ld.

The vowels **i** and **y** at the end of a syllable sometimes make the short vowel sounds **/ih/**, as in fam**i**ly and bic**y**cle, but usually make the long vowel sounds **/ee/** or **/iy/**, as in radi**o**, wind**y**, m**y**, and f**i**nal.

The letters **or** after **w** often make the **/uhr/** sound, as in w**or**d.

The **silent final e** causes the **preceding vowel** to make its **long sound**, as in m**a**de, **e**ve, d**i**me, h**o**pe, and **u**se.

The **silent final e** causes the **preceding c** to make the **/s/** sound, as in chan**c**e.

The **silent final e** causes the **preceding g** to make the **/j/** sound, as in chan**g**e.

Rules for Capital Letters

The first word in a sentence begins with a capital letter.

A proper noun begins with a capital letter.

The important words in titles of proper nouns begin with capital letters.

Interjections are usually capitalized.

All names referring to the true God and the Bible are capitalized.

The pronoun **I** is always written with a capital letter.

In the salutation of a letter, the first word and the name of the person begin with capital letters. In the complimentary close, the first word is capitalized.

Rules for Forming Plurals

Plurals are formed by adding **s** or **es** to the singular noun.

Simply add **s** to most nouns.

Add **es** to nouns ending with **ss**, **x**, **z**, **ch**, or **sh**.

Change **y** to **i** before adding **es** when a noun ends with **y** preceded by a consonant. When a noun ends with **y** preceded by a vowel, simply add **s**.

Usually when a noun ends with **f** or **fe**, simply add **s**. Sometimes change **f** or **fe** to **v** before adding **es**.

Add **es** to a noun ending with **o** preceded by a consonant, except some words, such as piano**s**. When a noun ends with **o** preceded by a vowel, simply add **s**.

The same rules for plurals of nouns apply to verbs in the present tense, third person, singular.

Rules for Adding Prefixes and Suffixes

Past-tense words ending in **-ed** make the /**ed**/ sound when the root ends with **d** or **t**; otherwise, the ending **-ed** makes the /**d**/ or /**t**/ sound.

Drop the **silent e** at the end of a word before adding a vowel suffix (prais**e**, prais**ing**).

Usually keep the **silent e** at the end of a word before adding a consonant suffix.

Change **y** to **i** before adding a suffix that does not begin with **i** (cr**y**, cr**i**ed).

Double the final consonant of a short-vowel one-syllable word before adding a vowel suffix (di**g**, di**gg**ing).

Double the final consonant of a two-syllable word ending with one consonant before adding a vowel suffix, except when the suffix changes the stress to the first syllable (refe**r**, refe**rr**ed, refe**r**ence).

When prefixes **dis**, **mis** and **un** are added to root words beginning with the same letter with which the prefix ends, this letter will be doubled (**unn**ecessary, **diss**olve, **miss**pell).

Rules for Identifying Types of Syllables

Closed Syllable (C)
ends with a consonant
vowel before the final consonant has a short vowel sound

Open Syllable (o)
ends with a vowel
vowel has a long vowel sound
can be just one letter if that letter is a vowel

Vowel-Consonant-e Syllable (vce)
final **e** is silent
vowel before silent final **e** has a long vowel sound

Diphthong Syllable (d)
diphthong (two vowels together) has one sound
diphthong syllable has one vowel sound

r-Combination Syllable (r-com)
at least one vowel followed by **r**
r gives the vowel a unique sound
r is after the vowel

Consonant-le Syllable (c-le)
syllable is at the end of a word
silent **e** is the only vowel in the syllable
syllable has no vowel sound
Only the consonant and the **l** are pronounced

Rules for Dividing Words into Syllables

A one-syllable word cannot be divided.

Each syllable has only one vowel sound.

Divide between the vowels when two vowels each make their own sound, as in qu**i**•**e**t.

Divide a compound word between the words.

Divide between the consonants when there are two or more consonants; however, do not divide two consonants that make one sound (a digraph) as in tel•e•**ph**one, or that blend together, as in sub•**tr**act

Divide before and after a vowel that makes its own sound, as in cav•**i**•ty.

Divide after the consonant when a short vowel sound is followed by a consonant and another vowel, as in H**eav**•**e**n.

Divide before the consonant when a long vowel sound is followed by a consonant and another vowel, as in p**a**•per.

When a word ends in **le** preceded by a consonant, divide the last syllable before the consonant, as in can•**dle** or fa•**ble**.

Divide between the base word and the prefix or suffix.

Rules for Accenting Syllables (for Parents)

Accent Mark
accent mark indicates the accented syllable

Accented Syllable
pronounced with a clear vowel sound

Unaccented Syllable
pronounced with a soft vowel sound

Primary Accent
strong stress on one of the syllables in a word

Secondary Accent
weaker stress on one of the syllables in a word

General Guideline
In two- and three-syllable words, accent the first syllable.
Then pronounce the first vowel as if it were a short, long, r-controlled, or double-vowel sound in a one-syllable word. If that doesn't make a recognizable word, accent the second syllable, and pronounce the second vowel according to its syllabic type.

ACCENT PATTERNS FOR TWO-SYLLABLE WORDS
Accent on the first syllable (' ___) The accent is usually on the first syllable in two-syllable words (stan' dard, sis' ter, dol' lar).

Accent on the second syllable (___ ') Two-syllable words that have a prefix in the first syllable and a root in the second syllable are usually accented on the second syllable (ex tend', con fuse').

Accent on either the first or second syllable (' ___ or ___ ') If a word can function as both noun and verb, the noun is accented on the prefix (con' duct) and the verb is accented on the root (con duct').

ACCENT PATTERNS FOR THREE-SYLLABLE WORDS
Accent on the first syllable (' ___ ___) The accent is usually on the first syllable in three-syllable words. The unaccented middle syllable has a soft sound (vis' i tor, char' ac ter).

Accent on the second syllable (___ ' ___) The accent is usually on the second syllable (the root) in words that contain a prefix, root, and suffix (de stroy' er, in ven' tor).

Rules for Accenting Syllables (for Parents)

ACCENT PATTERNS FOR FOUR-SYLLABLE WORDS (___ ___'___ ___)

The accent is usually on the second syllable in four-syllable words (in tel' li gence).

ACCENT PATTERNS FOR SOME THREE OR MORE SYLLABLE WORDS

Accent patterns for words longer than two syllables are often governed by a specific ending pattern or an unaccented vowel.

Accent with the ending -ic

Accent the syllable just before the ending -**ic** (fran' tic, e las' tic, en er get' ic, char ac ter is' tic).

Accent with the ending -ate /at/

In three-syllable words, the first syllable has a primary accent and -**ate** has a secondary (in' di cate)

In four-syllable words, the second syllable has a primary accent and -**ate** has a secondary (ac cen' tu ate).

Accent with schwa (soft) endings

Schwa endings (and schwa syllables) are never accented. The accent falls on another syllable in the word (pleas' ant, in' no cent, ex ter' nal, ap pren' tice).

Accent with the endings -tion, -sion, -cian

Accent the syllable just before the endings -**tion**, -**sion**, and -**cian** (pol lu' tion, im pres' sion, ad min is tra' tion, e lec tri' cian).

Accent with the ending -ity

Accent the syllable just before the ending -**ity** (qual' i ty, ac tiv' i ty, per son al' i ty).

Accent in words with an unaccented middle syllable

Accent the syllable just before the unaccented middle syllable with **i** as /**a**/, **i** as /**e**/, and **u** as /**a**/ or /**u**/ (sim' i lar, aud' i ence, par tic' u lar).

Accent in words with i as /y/

Accent the syllable just before the unaccented syllable with **i** as /**y**/ (com pan' ion, in con ven' ient, mem or a bil' i a).

Accent in words with ti or ci as /sh/ Accent the syllable just before a final syllable with **ti** or **ci** as /**sh**/ (fi nan' cial, pres i den' tial).

Art Credits

Page	Title	Artist
iv	Holy Family with St. John the Baptist	Gentileschi
5	Creation of the Heavens and Earth	Dore
6	The Garden of Paradise	Paulus
15	The Immaculate Conception	Tiepolo
16	Abraham Departs for Canaan	Molar
25	The Meeting of Abraham and Melchisedek	Bouts
26	Isaac and Jacob	Flinck
35	Joseph Is Placed in Charge of Egypt	Amiconi
36	The Sacrifice of Isaac	Champaigne
47	The Finding of Moses	Overbeck
48	The Ark of the Covenant	Tissot
57	The Walls of Jericho	Fouquet
58	Joshua Prays for the Sun to Stand Still	Martin
67	The Temple Pillars	Platzer
68	Presentation of Samuel to Eli	Doomer
77	Samuel Meets Saul	Tissot
78	Joseph Forgives His Brothers	von Cornelius
89	Death of Saul	Schonfeld
90	David Is Anointed	Rembrandt
99	David Slaying Goliath	Gentileschi
100	David Singing the Psalms	de Bray
109	The Wisdom of Solomon	Schopin
110	King Solomon and the Iron Worker	Schussele
119	King Solomon and the Queen of Sheba	Francken
120	The Death of Absolom	Viola
131	The King and the Prophet	Palma the Younger
132	Isaias	Michelangelo
141	Jonah Is Thrown to the Whale	Rubens
142	Tobias and the Angel	Strozzi
151	Job and His Friends	Repin
152	Babylonian Exile	Bendemann
161	Eleazar of Damascus	Dyce
162	Judas Maccabeus	Rubens